D1083263

THE
PERFUMED
GARDEN
of the
Shaykh
Nefzawi

To the pure all things are pure.
                    Quoted by Sir Richard Burton in his *Arabian Nights.*

There is little of love's language that I do not know ...
                    James Elroy Flecker – *Hassan.*

*The best books are those which startle you by contradicting your opinions
and beliefs. You learn more from your enemies than your friends.*
                    St. John Ervine (during a broadcast talk).

THE
PERFUMED
GARDEN

of the

Shaykh
Nefzawi

Translated by
SIR RICHARD F. BURTON
and
Edited with an Introduction and
Additional Notes by
ALAN HULL WALTON

NEVILLE SPEARMAN LTD

Printed in Great Britain by
Clarke, Doble and Brendon Ltd
Cattedown, Plymouth for
Neville Spearman Ltd
112 Whitfield Street, London W1

CONTENTS

THE PERFUMED GARDEN

6 Contents

INTRODUCTION

by

ALAN HULL WALTON

1. Introductory

T HE VENERABLE civilisation of India produced two ancient and celebrated manuals of erotic technique, conceived and worded in a spirit at once reverential and human. These are the famed *Kama Sutra* of Vatsyayana, and the lesser known, but still important *Ananga Ranga* of Kalyana Malla, or, as he is sometimes known, Kullianmull. They formed the first two volumes of Sir Richard Burton and Forster Fitzgerald Arbuthnot's admirable privately printed translations for the Kama Shastra Society of London and Benares.

The third volume, also privately printed in a limited edition for subscribers only, was issued during 1886. This was the comprehensive Arabian treatise known as *The Perfumed Garden*, compiled and written in a spirit comparable with that of the above-mentioned Sanskrit works, by the sixteenth century Shaykh Umar ibn Muhammed al-Nefzawi.*

In his *Arabian Nights* Burton has given us a brief but vivid glimpse of the glories of that memorable civilisation which

---

* The reason for Burton's retention of the French transliteration of Arabic names (i.e. 'Nefzaoui') is explained below, on page 19.

As regards the date of the composition of Nefzawi's book, investigations subsequent to the editions of Liseux and Burton, more especially those of the late Professor C. F. Seybold of Tübingen University, indicate that the work was probably written between the years 1394 and 1433. The matter is complicated by the fact that so little is known of the life of the author.

produced a rare flowering of genius in philosophy, medicine, chemistry, and astronomy:

> 'A splendid and glorious life was that of Baghdad in the days of the mighty Caliph, when the Capital had towered to the zenith of grandeur and was already trembling and tottering to the fall. The centre of human civilisation, which was then confined to Greece and Arabia, and the metropolis of an empire exceeding in extent the widest limits of Rome, it was essentially a city of pleasure, a Paris of the ninth century. The "Palace of Peace" (Dar al-Salam), worthy successor of Babylon and Ninevah, which had outrivalled Damascus, the "Smile of the Prophet", and Kufah, the successor of Hira and the magnificent creation of Caliph Omar, possessed unrivalled advantages of site and climate.
>
> 'The Tigris – Euphrates Valley, where the fabled Garden of Eden has been placed, in early ages succeeded the Nile Valley as a great centre of human development; and the prerogative of a central and commanding position still promises it . . . a magnificent future . . . The city of palaces and government offices, hotels and pavilions, mosques and colleges, kiosks and squares, bazaars and markets, pleasure grounds and orchards, adorned with all the graceful charms which Saracenic architecture had borrowed from the Byzantines, lay couched upon the banks of the Dijlah-Hiddekel under a sky of marvellous purity and in a climate which makes mere life a "kayf" – the luxury of tranquil enjoyment. It was surrounded by far extending suburbs, like Rusafah on the Eastern side, and villages like Baturanjah, dear to the votaries of pleasure; and with the roar of a gigantic capital mingled the hum of prayer, the trilling of birds, the thrilling of harp and lute, the shrilling of pipes, the witching strains of the professional Almeh, and the minstrel's lay . . .' *

Such, then, was the ambiance of that mighty Arab civilisation which, despite the Mongol conquest of Baghdad in 1258, and many other vicissitudes duly noted in history, continued to produce a heritage of noteworthy and distinguished work in the fields of philosophy, medicine, and science generally. The names of the contributors to this heritage need not concern us here, except to say that Nefzawi, born in the sixteenth century, was their direct descendant; and it is largely due to his book, and to

* See Burton, *The Book of the Thousand Nights and a Night* . . . Benares, MDCCCLXXXV, Printed by the Kama Shastra Society for Private Subscribers Only (Sixteen vols.). The quotation is taken from the famous *Terminal Essay* (pages 173-174) which occupies the greater portion of vol. ten (vols. eleven to sixteen constitute the *Supplemental Nights*).

Burton's masterly translation of the *Arabian Nights,* that the West has come to a reasonably precise, accurate, and systematised knowledge of Mohammedan sexual life and thought.

During the two hundred years of the Crusades – that is from 1097 to the end of the Christian domination of Palestine and Syria in approximately 1291 – certain Oriental customs and ways of thought slowly began to permeate Europe through France and Sicily. Likewise various Oriental products and luxuries began to be imported by the wealthy through the same channels. Throughout two centuries the Mediterranean was crossed and recrossed by convoys of caravelles, bringing from Marseilles, Pisa, Genoa, and Venice, food, arms and soldiers. But these vessels did not return empty to Europe. They returned laden with silks from China, carpets from Persia; and, not least, porcelain, muslin, fabrics, cloths, spices, fruits, perfumes and – equally precious – thoughts, ideas, and information from Arabia.

As the Rev. G. Margoliouth has pointed out, in his Introduction to Rodwell's translation of the *Koran**: 'Research has shown that what European scholars knew of Greek philosophy, of mathematics, astronomy, and like sciences, for several centuries before the Renaissance, was, roughly speaking, all derived from Latin treatises ultimately based upon Arabic originals; and it was the *Koran* which, though indirectly, gave the first impetus to these studies among the Arabs and their allies. Linguistic investigations, poetry, and other branches of literature, also made their appearance soon after or simultaneously with the publication of the *Koran*; and the literary movement thus initiated has resulted in some of the finest products of genius and learning.'

The importation of ideas, goods, and commodities, as a result of these Holy Wars, slowly began to produce more widespread effects; for the walled and moated castles of France, England, and other parts of Europe, gradually ceased to be chill and dismal dwellings whose cold walls stank with dampness and mould. The

* Rodwells' *Koran* (Everyman edition), London, Dent (New York, Dutton), 1939, page 9.

icy flagstones of their floors were no longer bare, or simply
strewn with rushes – they were covered with the richness,
warmth, and comfort of magnificent draperies, carpets, and rugs.
Much softer, lighter, finer woollen materials made their appearance, and these were coloured with brilliant dyes from the East.
The dull and frequently coarse homespun cloth worn by our
ancestors was replaced by silk and other rare fabrics; and, following the heroines of the Bible, our women began to care for their
bodies, to wash and perfume them,* and to comb and dress their
hair.

The culinary arts improved, new dishes began to make their
appearance, and hitherto unknown fruits and vegetables graced
our tables: apricots, cherries, melons, artichokes, and rice. Not
only Crusaders, but also pilgrims, brought home with them silk-
worms, seeds of vegetables and flowering plants, perfumes,
combs, scrolls, and delicate ornaments decorated with fantastic
animals, unusual designs, and even the representation of exotic
embraces.

Naturally shipowners became rich, the vaults of bankers began
to overflow, and the blue-print was laid for our contemporary
occidental civilisation, with its luxury trades, its learning, its
status symbols, its science, its opulence, its middle-classes, and
its wealth. The rediscovery, during the Renaissance, of the
glories of ancient Greece and Rome, merely accelerated a trend
which had already been established.

But, as has already been hinted, the war lords of the Crusades
brought back more than material goods. They had discovered
that love was an art, and that the sexual act could be a science.
They revealed new attitudes in their approaches to their wives;
and traditional activity became tempered by innovation. The
beautiful and accomplished Arabian, Numidian, and Syrian in-

* For the early Christian and mediaeval condemnation of bathing, and
for the introduction of the bath into Europe by the Crusaders (the baths
of Rome had long been forgotten) see Havelock Ellis, *Studies in the
Psychology of Sex*, New York, Random House, 1936, vol. two, part 1,
pages 21-40.

mates of cloistered harems had not been slow to educate the uncouth nobility of Europe – together with their brutish and drunken serving-men and foot-soldiers – in all the niceties of erotic refinement, from the personal cleanliness essential in such refinements, to all the delights of delayed pleasure, continued and varied foreplay, and the joys arising from an unselfish and applied technique.

Thus it will be seen that many of our present sexual attitudes have their distant origins in Arabia, India, Greece, and Rome. These were modified, on reception into our colder climes, by native interpretation, convention, religion, and practice. The Moorish influence in Spain also contributed, slowly and indirectly, to the dissemination of Oriental ideas.

A carefully compiled, systematised, and detailed manual of Arabian sex practice was not, however, known in Europe until a Frenchman's discovery, during the nineteenth century, of Nefzawi's classic, *The Perfumed Garden*. The story of his discovery of this work, and of its introduction to the French and English speaking peoples, is interesting enough to merit relation in some detail.

2. The Story of the Book

SOME TIME PRIOR to the year 1850, a French army officer, apparently stationed in Algeria, came across a manuscript copy of a work in arabic entitled: *Al Raud al atir wa nuzhat al Khatir*. This was, of course, the celebrated *Perfumed Garden**, at that period unknown to the West. The officer, whose identity has

---

* As readers of Burton, Payne, and Lane – not to mention Galland and Mardrus – will have realised, the transliteration of arabic words varies from one author to another. Wedeck (*Dictionary of Aphrodisiacs*, New York, Philosophical Library, 1960; London, Peter Owen, 1962) gives the title of the *Garden* as follows: *Er Roud El Aater P'nezaha El Khater*. It can be translated as: *The Perfumed Garden, Man's Heart to Gladden*; and has also been rendered: *The Scented Garden* (or *Perfumed Garden*) *for the Soul's Delectation*. In one version the final words become: '. . . *for the Soul's Recreation*'. There exist a series of variants, chiefly in references to the book by other writers.

never satisfactorily been solved, and whose name is hidden under the cryptical designation, 'Monsieur le Baron R * * *, Capitaine d'Etat major', immediately became fascinated by the book; and, realising something of its importance, set to work to translate it into his native tongue, completing his task about 1850. Although little is known about the officer in question, his work would seem to indicate a man of good family and considerable education.

Publication, however, was delayed for approximately a quarter of a century. Partly, perhaps, owing to a natural reticence on the part of the translator, undoubtedly complicated by the very real difficulty of finding a suitably equipped printing press in Algeria. At length four French officers, who were also students and scholars, collaborated in the unique venture of lithographing the volume on the official machines of the French Government. The operation was performed in secret, but ended abruptly when their activities were discovered by their commanding officer.

This edition, known as the 'autograph edition', and the first translation ever to be made, consisted of only 35 copies. The title-page, which gives no indication as to date or place of publication – though it has been ascertained that the volume definitely first appeared at Algiers during 1876 – runs as follows:

LE JARDIN PARFUME (AL-RAUD AL-ATIR) *Par le Sidi Mohammed el-Nafzaoui: Ouvrage du Cheikh, l'Iman, le Savant, le très-Erudit, le très Intelligent, le très-Véridique Sidi Mohammed el-Nafzaoui que Dieu très-Elevé lui fasse Miséricorde par sa Puissance. Amen. Traduit de l'Arabe par Monsieur le Baron R * * *, Capitaine d'Etat major.*

The contents of the 'autograph edition' consist of 283 pages of text, 15 pages of *avis au lecteur*, 2 portraits, 13 *hors textes* on blue paper, 43 erotic illustrations in the text, and, at the end of the book, about 10 pages of errata, with a *Table of Contents* and some blank leaves.

This original lithograph edition was counterfeited in Paris during 1885, the counterfeit being, in all respects, so well reproduced in facsimile, that it is extremely difficult to distinguish between the original and the fake. The facsimile, however, contains an extra portrait, and its cover bears a phallic watermark. Carrington describes the watermark as being 'a butterfly'; and it is possible that some of the paper used for covers did have a butterfly watermark.

In the year previous to the issue of the counterfeit edition an element of mystery enters the story; for it was in the August of that year that the distinguished novelist, Guy de Maupassant, wrote personally to a Paris publisher, suggesting a reprint of the text of the lithograph edition – which he had just discovered. The text of Maupassant's letter follows:

> *'Oasis de Bou Sàada,*
> *25 aout, 1884.*

Monsieur et chèr Editeur,

Je reçois aujourd'hui en plein Sahara votre carte postale.

Envoyez-moi, je vous prie, *le recueil chez moi,* à Paris, 83, rue Dulong (Batignolles), c'est encore le plus sûr. Je le trouverai dans un mois à mon retour.

Maintenant autre chose. Je viens de découvrir ici un livre arabe, lubrique, remarquablement traduit par un officier supérieur français.

L'histoire de ce livre est curieuse. Un écrivain arabe allait être mis à mort par ordre d'un bey (celui de Tunis, je crois) quand il obtint sa grâce à la condition qu'il écrirait un livre capable de réveiller les passions mourantes de son souverain.

Il a écrit ce livre et fut gracié. Les dessins de cette traduction sont faits par un officier d'Etat major. Tous sont remarquables. Un d'eux me paraît être un vrai chef-d'oeuvre. Il représente deux êtres épuisés après l'étreinte.

Ce livre absolument inconnu de tout le monde me paraît singulièrement intéressant *pour les amateurs de raretés.* Vous irait-il de le publier?

L'officier traducteur hésite beaucoup, ayant grand peur que son nom soit prononcé. Je lui ai affirmé que dans le cas ou cet ouvrage vous agréerait, il pourrait être assuré de la plus absolue discrétion.

Malheureusement il n'a pas osé traduire un des chapitres concernant un vice fort commun en ce pays – "la Pédérastie";* mais, en somme, le livre est, en son genre un des plus curieux qu'on puisse trouver.

---

* This statement that the translator 'has not dared to translate a chapter concerning a vice very common in this country – that of "Pederasty",' will be returned to later in the text of this introduction. The statement made by Maupassant is, however, not quite correct, for what the officer omitted was not an entire chapter, but simply the very long final section of the twenty-first, and closing, chapter.

Si cette trouvaille vous tentait, vous pourriez écrire directment de ma part à M. le Commandant Maréchal, Commandant Supérieur du Cercle Militaire de Bou-Sàada (Algérie).*

M. le Commandant Maréchal ne voudrait point entendre parler de question d'argent. Vous lui donneriez tout simplement quelques exemplaires.

Une autre question serait embarrassante. Il a fait autographier ce livre, en secret, par des subordonnés et il hésiterait beaucoup à se separer de ce volume original relié magnifiquement. Pour les dessins cela pourrait créer un embarras.

Veuillez toujours me répondre un mot, *car si la chose ne vous convenait pas, je connais quelqu'un qui la prendrait, immédiatement.*†

Recevez, cher Monsieur, l'expression de mes sentiments empressés et tout dévoués.

GUY DE MAUPASSANT

Du 5 septembre au Ier octobre on peut m'écrire à Erbalunga, commune de Brando, près Bastia, *Corse*.'‡

What remains uncertain is whether Maupassant was writing to the publisher who issued the counterfeit edition of 1885, to Isidore Liseux (who eventually set the book in an attractive typeface, publishing a strictly limited edition aimed at scholars and collectors), or to his own publisher. If to his own publisher, then the remark that '*if the suggestion doesn't suit you, then I know someone who will take it up immediately,*' must apply either to the counterfeit publisher, or to Liseux....

Isidore Liseux was a publisher, scholar, and bibliophile of some distinction, specialising in the issue of rare, forgotten, or curious works of literary interest. He frequently enjoyed the collaboration of another learned bibliophile, Alcide Bonneau (who

---

* It has been said that the Commandant Maréchal was not the translator of the book, but one of the four officers who collaborated in the production of the 'autograph edition'. Maupassant's letter, nevertheless, would seem to indicate otherwise.

† The italics represent the underlining made by Maupassant in his letter.

‡ The text of this letter also appears in Louis Perceau: *Bibliographie du Roman Erotique au XIXe Siècle*: Donnant une description complète de tous les . . . ouvrages en prose . . . publiés en Français, de 1800 à nos jours, et de toutes leurs réimpressions. Two volumes. Paris, Georges Fourdrinier, 1930. (1,050 numbered sets printed.)

contributed many of the prefaces or introductions to the chosen volumes). These were always superbly printed on magnificent paper with ample margins, and generally decorated with elegant head and tailpieces, and ornamental initial letters. In the case of translations from Latin and Italian works of the Renaissance, or later, the original text was usually printed on opposite pages, much as in our present-day Loeb Series. The editing and annotation was always scholarly; and, owing to this publisher's habit of limiting most of his editions to a comparatively small number of copies – though on occasion he did reprint – most of his volumes have achieved the distinction of rarity, and are now eagerly sought by scholars and collectors alike.

Amongst his noteworthy printings one finds works such as the *De Demonialitate* of the Reverend Father Ludovico Maria Sinistrari of Ameno, a seventeenth-century theological treatise, the manuscript of which was discovered by Liseux himself while browsing, during 1872, in the shop of a second-hand bookseller in London's Euston Road. It had never previously been printed, but appeared with an accurate French translation facing the Latin text, an interesting introduction, and a biographical notice, during 1875. An English translation (also with Latin text *en face*) was published by Liseux, at Paris, in 1879. Among his other noteworthy publications were editions of Poggio (1879), in two volumes (with Latin text); a French translation (with Italian text) of the *Ragionamenti* of Aretino, in six volumes (1882); and a French translation (with Latin text) of the fifteenth century *Hecatelegium* of Pacifico Massimi (1885).*

---

* The bibliography of Liseux is lengthy, and sometimes a little complicated (he published, for example, more than one edition of Aretino, and more than one of Chorier's *Luisa Sigea* – some with the original text, and some without; and each differing from the other in any case). All that can be done above is to indicate some of his more important issues.

Among his valuable contributions to what might be termed bibliophilic literature are the four volumes entitled : *La Curiosité Littéraire et Bibliographique* : Articles Littéraires, Extraits et Analyses d'Ouvrages Curieux. Notices de Livres Rares, Anecdotes, Etc. Paris, 1880-1883. These volumes, well known to, and mentioned by Burton in his *Nights*, contain a mass of

Whatever the import of Maupassant's laudatory letter, Liseux was the publisher who first set *The Perfumed Garden* in type, correcting and revising the text, and issuing it in a superb edition limited to 220 copies. The title-page of this first printed edition runs as follows:

LE JARDIN PARFUME DU CHEIKH NEFZAOUI: *Manuel d'Erotologie Arabe: XVI Siècle. Traduction revue et corrigé.* Paris, Isidore Liseux, 1886.

The Liseux text was reprinted at Paris during 1904 in a 'Réimpression conforme à l'édition publiée en 1886'. No publisher's name was given, and Liseux was certainly not responsible for the reprint, as he had died about ten years previously.

Further excellent and unlimited reprints of his edition were published at Paris by the Bibliothèque des Curieux – in their 'Maitres de l'Amour' series – during 1911 and 1922. The latest reprint is an expensive and well-produced bound edition, recently issued at Paris by the 'Cercle du Livre Précieux'.

This Liseux revised version of the original 1850 translation immediately drew Burton's attention. He mentions it in volume X of his *Arabian Nights* (page 133), and mistakenly refers to it as being issued in 1866, instead of in 1886. In the same place he draws attention to the Kama Shastra Society edition of the English translation of *The Perfumed Garden*. This was, of course, made direct from the Liseux volume published during 1886, being anonymously translated by Burton, and privately issued from London during the same year.

At this point it seems convenient briefly to examine the constitution and aims of the so-called Kama Shastra Society. As W. G. Archer has pointed out in his admirable Preface to the

rare material of extremely varied character, including the complete Latin text, with French translation, of the virtually unknown *Mémoires de Chorier*, essays by Alcide Bonneau on juxtalinear translation (Horace and *Orlando Furioso*), and an essay entitled: *La Préface de Mademoiselle de Maupin, dans l'édition originale et dans les éditions actuelles*, etc., etc. The volumes contain, in fact, so many extracts and essays, that it is impossible to detail them here.

reprint of Burton and Arbuthnot's *Kama Sutra*,* the aim of the Society is sufficiently indicated by its name. *Kama*, in Sanskrit, may be translated as 'love', or 'pleasure', in the sensual sense of these terms. *Shastra* may be rendered as 'scripture', or 'doctrines'. Thus the aim of the Society was the translation and issue of rare and important Oriental works concerning love and sex. As to its members, there were two only: Sir Richard Francis Burton, and his friend of many years, Forster Fitzgerald Arbuthnot. With reservations a third name might be added – that of Richard Monckton Milnes, who later became Lord Houghton. Milnes was an educated and distinguished English gentleman whose discerning love for the erotic in literature caused him to become the invisible patron of the Society, and stimulated him to support Burton's pioneer researches in the new science of sexology.

Five titles, in all, were privately issued by the Kama Shastra Society to its subscribers. These, with their dates, were:

1. *The Kama Sutra*, 1883.
2. *The Ananga Ranga*, 1885.†
3. *The Perfumed Garden*, 1886.
4. *The Beharistan*, 1887.
5. *The Gulistan*, 1888.‡

The title-page of Burton's translation of the *Arabian Nights* also bore the name of the Society. This, however, as Penzer has

---

* The interested reader should see: *The Kama Sutra of Vatsyayana*, Translated by Sir Richard Burton and F. F. Arbuthnot, Edited with a Preface by W. G. Archer; Introduction by K. M. Panikkar. London, George Allen & Unwin Ltd., 1963 (pages 11-17, et seq.). The importance of Archer's Preface cannot be overestimated, and his edition is infinitely preferable to the original of 1883.

† Translated, as was the *Kama Sutra*, from the Sanskrit.

‡ The *Beharistan* and the *Gulistan* (by Jami and Sa'di, respectively) were both translated from the Persian by Edward Rehatsek, a mutual friend of Arbuthnot and Burton, who had spent many years in India. A list of his many writings is given by Arbuthnot in an article in the *Journal of the Royal Asiatic Society* (July, 1892, page 592) entitled: *The Life and Labours of Mr. Rehatsek*.

B

pointed out,* was simply because Burton did not wish to employ
the name of a publisher or printer – he, himself, in this instance
being the publisher. Thus the work cannot rightly be considered
as an issue of the Society. Its binding and format were, moreover, quite different from the smaller format and full vellum
bindings of the five titles listed above.

Almost immediately on the appearance of the Liseux version
of *The Perfumed Garden*, Burton decided, as has been indicated
above, to translate direct from the French. There can be no doubt
that this edition ranked as high in his estimation as had the
'autograph edition' in the opinion of Guy de Maupassant. The
first Kama Shastra Society edition was issued in parts (seven or
ten), with paper covers in different tints of grey and fawn. The
title-page of each part was printed in black ink, and this page
was reproduced, within a fancy border, on the outer wrapper.

The second edition appeared later in the same year, this time
as a volume bound in full white vellum with bevelled edges.
There was a plain ruled border on the front cover in gold, and on
the back cover in blind. The lettering on the spine was also in
gold. The size was 5⅛″ × 7⅞″, and all edges were uncut. The
title-page was as for the first edition, with the exception that
the words '*Revised and Corrected Translation*' have been added.
It reads:

THE PERFUMED GARDEN OF THE CHEIKH NEFZAOUI: A *Manual of
Arabian Erotology (XVI Century): Revised and Corrected Translation.
Cosmopoli: MDCCCLXXXVI: for the Kama Shastra Society of London
and Benares, and for Private circulation only.* (Pagination: xvi + 256).

The translation, which follows the French of the Liseux text
very closely, is yet one more example of the success which can
be achieved by the translation of a work from one language into
another, and then into a third. Some beautiful and noteworthy
examples of this method were produced by E. Powys Mathers

* Norman M. Penzer, M.A., F.R.G.S., F.G.S. (etc.): *An Annotated Bibliography of Sir Richard Francis Burton, K.C.M.G.* . . . London, A. M. Philpot
Ltd., 1923 (the edition was limited to 500 signed and numbered copies),
see page 162.

who, in 1927, published English versions of the *Kuttanimatam* of Damodaragupta and the *Samayamatrika* of Kshemendra, which he translated via the French translations of Louis de Langle.* The practice is not at all unusual, and has resulted in some exceptionally fine versions of foreign classics, such as Bernard Miall's English rendering of the Chinese *Chin P'ing Mei*, which he made from Franz Kuhn's lengthy abridged German translation.†

This brings us, indirectly, to the transliteration of Nefzawi's name, and Burton's retention of the French form (*Nefzaoui*). In English the name has been rendered: *Nefzawi*, *Nefzawih*, and *Nafzawi* – and Burton had, already, in a lengthy Latin footnote on circumcision (printed in his *Pilgrimage to Al-Madinah‡*), referred to the work of the 'Shaykh al-Nafzawi' (spelt thus). It seems likely that the translator wished to maintain the anonymity he had shared with Arbuthnot in their Kama Shastra edition of the *Kama Sutra*. And what could be more misleading, and more suited to such a purpose, than the retention of the French transliteration?

This was not, of course, the first time that the French forms of Arabic words had been retained in an English translation. The

---

* These appear together in the first two volumes of the twelve volume anthology: *Eastern Love*, Translated by E. Powys Mathers, London, John Rodker, 1927-29 (other volumes included: *The Zenan-Nahmeh* of Fazil Bey, the anonymous Persian *Ta'dib ul-Nisvan*, the *Kissat al-'Ara'is*, the *Loves of Radha and Krishna*, ninety short tales from the Arabic, and various translations of Chinese, Japanese, and Cambodian works (including poetry). All were made from French versions).

† *Chin P'ing Mei*: The Adventurous History of Hsi Men . . . With an Introduction by Arthur Waley (translated by Bernard Miall from the abridged version of Franz Kuhn [Insel-Verlag, Leipzig]). London, John Lane, 1939 – reprinted 1942, 1950, 1952, etc.

Judging from a comparison of texts, an excellent English version of the twelfth book of the Greek Anthology appears to have been made from a French translation published during 1910. This was published at London in a beautiful limited edition, but without date (*c*. 1930).

‡ *Personal Narrative of a Pilgrimage to Al Madinah and Meccah* by Capt. Sir Richard F. Burton . . . with an Introduction by Stanley Lane-Poole. London, G. Bell & Sons Ltd., 1898 (two vols.). This is a reprint of the 'Memorial' (and best) edition of the work. My own copy (1926 reprint) misprints 'Nawawi' for 'Nafzawi'. See vol. two, pages 19 and 20.

example had been set during the eighteenth century in the English translation made from Galland's French version of the *Arabian Nights*, (originally published in the French language between 1704 and 1717).

By 1888, however, a thousand sets of the sixteen volumes of Burton's literal, unabridged, and unexpurgated translation of the *Arabian Nights* had been issued. He had attained, on every count, the ultimate in acceptance, distinction, and celebrity. And what was more natural than that, despite the undignified and moronic antics of an uncultured yet powerful Mrs. Grundy, he should become more brave? Accordingly, in this same year, he began a new translation of *The Perfumed Garden*; this time, apparently, direct from an Arabic manuscript, and with much less concern for secrecy. Why, it may be asked, was this new version necessary? The answer, I think, lies in that sentence in the letter of Guy de Maupassant which stated that the original French translator had 'not dared to translate a chapter concerning a vice very common in this country – that of "Pederasty" '.

Almost throughout his life Burton had been extremely interested in the subject of homosexuality. He may be considered, in fact, the pioneer in the serious study of this subject in England; for, without doubt, he paved the way for that classic volume which forms the second part of Havelock Ellis's monumental *Studies in the Psychology of Sex*.*

The new *Garden*, then, was to contain the whole of the very considerable portion of the twenty-first chapter concerning homosexuality, which had been eliminated by the modest and anonymous French translator. Burton died in 1890, leaving the new manuscript of Nefzawi not quite complete. As is now well known, his wife immediately burnt the book, thus incurring the wrath and (quite justifiable) exasperation of innumerable eminent scholars throughout the world. In the long run, however, not much appears to have been lost; for according to Dr. Grenfell Baker, who throughout the period that Sir Richard was

* i.e. *Sexual Inversion*, London, 1897 (and Philadelphia, 1901).

engaged on this new version daily had intimate converse with him concerning its contents, 'it was merely a greatly annotated edition of that issued in 1886' – plus, of course, the controversial section on pederasty. Baker continues: 'The *Nights* had contained many curious and extremely interesting notes, but there was still a large amount that had not been published, and such a work as *The Perfumed Garden* offered a good opportunity for putting on record what remained partly in Burton's private note-books and partly in his great brain.'* Penzer, quoting Dr. Baker, adds: 'Thus, not only did anthropological customs, curious vices, and personal experiences connected with Arabia and the Arabs go into the work, but comparisons and similies were made with those of other Eastern countries, as also with some Western ones, in both classical and modern times, as for example, Babylonia, Egypt, China, and central America.

'To give an example, Burton had already (*Supplemental Nights*, vol. one, pages 70-2) written a long note on the history of eunuchs. Some time after he discovered an article by G. Carter Stent in the "Journ. North-China Branch Roy. As. Soc.," N.S. XI, 1877 (pages 143-84), on Chinese eunuchs.

'This is a most interesting article, and, I believe, the only one of its kind ever written. The information contained therein was certainly new to Burton, and it is marked (in his copy in the Kensington Library) ready for amalgamation in the new edition of the *Garden*.'

There is no reason to doubt Dr. Grenfell Baker's statement that the burnt manuscript of the new version of *The Perfumed Garden* (or, as it was now to be called, *The Scented Garden*), was simply a revision of the translation from the Liseux edition, considerably expanded by many additional footnotes, and with the long section on pederasty restored – in a translation specially made by Burton, direct from an Arabic manuscript. There was also a new, and very full Introduction by Burton, said to consist

* Norman M. Penzer: *An Annotated Bibliography of Sir Richard Francis Burton* . . . London, A. M. Philpot Ltd., 1923. – See page 176 for the comments of both Baker and Penzer.

largely of extracts translated from the works of Numa
Numantius*, a learned German legal official, himself sexually
inverted, who spent the greater part of his life in the exposition
and defence of homosexual love.

From this it will be realised that the general reader has probably lost little by Lady Burton's hasty action. The loss, of course,
for scholars, cannot precisely be estimated. All we can be certain
of is that Burton reiterated to Dr. Baker the fact that this extra-
annotated version of the book was his *magnum opus*: 'I have put
my whole life and all my life-blood into that *Scented Garden*; it
is my great hope that I shall live by it. It is the crown of my life.'

And despite his wife's efforts to consign the *Garden* to oblivion,
he *has* lived by it; for, equally with the *Arabian Nights*, the Kama
Shastra edition of Nefzawi – however much it may lack the controversial pederastic section – remains his most celebrated work.

All we can now do regarding the lost version is to agree with
Penzer that 'It is . . . most dangerous and wrong to burn unpub-
lished MSS of an author, even if the person doing so be the man's

* Karl Heinrich Ulrichs, who wrote under the pseudonym of Numa
Numantius, was born during 1825 near Aurich. Havelock Ellis also devoted
some sympathetic attention to the study of his works: 'The man, however, who more than anyone else brought to light the phenomena of
sexual inversion, had not been concerned either with the medical or the
criminal aspects of the matter . . . From 1864 onward, at first under the
name of "Numa Numantius" and subsequently under his own name,
Ulrichs published, in various parts of Germany, a long series of works
dealing with this question, and made various attempts to obtain a
revision of the legal position of the sexual invert in Germany . . . Ulrichs
appears to have been a man of most brilliant ability, and his knowledge
is said to have been of almost universal extent; he was not only well
versed in his own special subjects of jurisprudence and theology, but in
many branches of natural science, as well as archaeology; he was also
regarded as the best Latinist of his time. In 1880 he left Germany and
settled in Naples, and afterwards at Aquilla in the Abruzzi . . . He died
in 1895 (see: *Jahrbuch für sexuelle Zwischenstufen*, Bd. i, 1899, page 36).'
– Ellis, *Studies, etc., Sexual Inversion*, Philadelphia, F. A. Davis, 1915 (or
Random House reprint of 1936). Edward Carpenter also deals with Ulrichs
in his *Intermediate Sex*, London, Allen & Unwin, 1921 reprint, pages 157-
60. Ulrichs's works include: *Vindex* (1864), *Inclusa* (the same year), *Forma-
trix* (1865), *Vindicta* (the same year), and *Prometheus* (1870). There are
many more. Most were reprinted at Leipzig by Max Spohr during 1898.
Their interest today is very largely historical.

own wife. With regard to the work in question it is, I think, obvious that Lady Burton should have sent it (and any other similar works) to the Council either of the Royal Asiatic Society or the Anthropological Institute. . . .'*

The remainder of the story can be dealt with briefly.

Towards the end of the nineteenth century an Englishman named Charles Carrington settled in Paris with the express intent of publishing rather elaborate editions of works likely to be pro- hibited in Victorian England.† Some of his issues were, to say the least, beautiful examples of the printer's art; nevertheless, Carrington remained to the end, something of an opportunist. He naturally heard about Lady Burton's destruction of the newly annotated *Garden*, together with its Introduction and the for- bidden chapter. And he immediately set to work to replace the loss. His method of going about this was to procure what he described as an 'absolutely unique' copy, in Arabic, 'composed of four large royal octavo volumes of about 500 pages each. This manuscript was done by Abd-Ul-Fattah (of the Azhar Univer- sity, Cairo) and M. l'abbé Katib, a Syrian Calligraphist. . . The text was read over and revised by Prof. Seligsohn (a profound Russian Orientalist and once pupil of Prof. Hartwig Derenbourg, the celebrated Arabist of the Sorbonne).

'This is the *fullest and most correct* Arabic MS known‡ of this famous production. . . In all probability it is the most complete in existence.'

* Penzer, op. cit., pages 175-76.
† Brief details of Carrington's career can be found in Alec Craig: *The Banned Books of England* . . . London, George Allen & Unwin, 1962, pages 70-71. While it cannot be denied that Carrington published some trivia, not to say rubbish, he also issued some remarkably fine and scholarly editions. His anonymously translated *Petronius*, with its learned notes, has never been bettered. Likewise his editions of Brantôme and Straparola, and of Rosenbaum's history of venereal disease (*The Plague of Lust in Classical Antiquity*), remain valued treasures for the bibliophile and scholar. It is said that Oscar Wilde made some of the translations published by him, though this may be doubted. On the other hand, Alfred Allinson, the Oxford M.A., certainly did produce some very good translations for this remarkable, if sometimes shady, *'éditeur sublime'*.

‡ The italics are those of Carrington, and obviously employed as a bait.

Carrington announced this work, which was a new translation by an anonymous hand, as to appear in three volumes. The whole affair, as we shall see, was shrouded in mystery, and only the first volume appeared. Its half-title bore the words: *The Scented Garden Man's Heart to Gladden* (which was, as we know, to have been the title of Sir Richard Burton's revised edition). The title-page, printed in red and black, read as follows:

> Privately Issued: *The Perfumed Garden for the Soul's Delectation*: Translated from the Arabic of the Shaykh Nafzawi (XV saec.) The First of Three Volumes. *'This is no baby's book.'* (Sir R. F. Burton.) Paris and Benares. The Kamashastra Society, 1907.*

The volume, printed in red and black throughout on the presses of the Imprimerie Veuve Félix Guy et Cie at Alençon, consisted of 283 pages. The first 112 pages were taken up by a detailed Foreword containing some accurate information, a little twaddle, and not a few purposely erroneous and misleading statements concerning previous editions of the Garden – all of them calculated to promote the sales of the Carrington version at the expense of the Liseux and the original Burton issues. No scholar or bibliophile, however, could ever be deceived by such calculated and incredible nonsense. Penzer, who mentions the volume without describing it, simply comments:

> 'The edition has absolutely no right to use the name of Burton's Society, and it is one which on inspection collectors and students will leave alone.'†

The text translated from Nefzawi in this first volume extends only to the end of his third chapter, and is copiously peppered with curious footnotes contrivedly – but not always with success – fashioned after those which have made Burton's *Nights* such a valuable contribution to anthropology.

The second and third volumes never appeared. The reason remains, up to the moment, something of a mystery; for the work had been translated in its entirety, and a complete set of galley-proofs exists to prove it. The translation had obviously

---

* 'Kamashastra' is spelled thus, and not as Burton had it: *Kama Shastra*.
† Penzer, op. cit., page 175.

been completed prior to 1899, for in that year Carrington advertised the sale of the above-mentioned Arabic manuscript:

> Mr. Chas. Carrington begs to inform Book-buyers that . . . he has (for sale) a complete and most beautiful manuscript of the above-named marvellous compendium of oriental sexuology . . . bound in *whole green morocco*, with flaps after the Eastern style, and four strong artistic cases made by Bretault (of Paris), the title of the work in arabic monogram on both sides of each volume . . . Price (of the four volumes complete) £100 . . . (*etc.*)

Another enigma is the delay of approximately eight years between the apparent completion of the translation and the publication of the first and only volume.

Shortly after the First World War, Carrington, now blind and suffering in health, gave his business into the hands of two young assistants, one of whom established himself later in Mexico. Some years ago I was told that an antiquarian book-dealer in Mexico (most likely the gentleman referred to above) possessed not only the Carrington Arabic Manuscript, but also a complete set of galleys of the translation (vols. one to three), and that he was offering these for sale at something like £500. The anonymous translator bearing no comparison with Burton, I was not sufficiently interested to enquire further into the matter. The only outstanding virtue of his first volume, in fact, lies in his rendering of various passages into *saj'a* (the Arabic rhymed prose so familiar to readers of Burton's *Nights*.) These efforts, nevertheless, are apt to be clumsy, and cannot be said to contribute any noteworthy attraction to a volume whose only claim to distinction lies in its rarity.

For the rest there have been thousands upon thousands of copies of cheap and shoddy paper-back reprints of Burton's Kama Shastra edition, generally imperfect, and usually making their appearance in Paris. Some such paper-backs were not even reprints of Burton, but mediocre hack-translations made from the Liseux edition. One such, which appeared about 1930 at Paris, bore the imprint: 'Les Publications Parisiennes,' and the indubitably false statement: 'Privately Issued'. It was stitched in dull green paper wrappers, and totalled 191 pages, uncut. Moreover, almost every page of the text abounded, as do many of these tourist-aimed products, in misprints and lacunae.*

A pleasanter reprint, more or less textually accurate, and following the original Kama Shastra edition (even to title-page), though set in a different type-face, printed on cheaper paper, and bound in paper-covered boards, was issued during the 1920's. This was clandestinely printed at either Leicester or Birmingham, and might claim to be a comparatively good substitute for the original Kama Shastra edition of 1886.

All of which goes to prove one very important truth – the fact that, just as our antiquated and unenlightened laws regarding homosexuality do not, and never have reduced the incidence of homosexual activity – but, on the contrary, have provided a munificent living for countless blackmailers – so did our old laws concerning obscenity in literature (laws which so often prevented the publication in England of serious, valuable, and important works) dismally fail in their pretended aims. For what they achieved in the long run was the continued, if indirect, publicity of works which might otherwise have passed almost unnoticed; together with the open printing abroad, in English (and the clandestine printing at home), of such works – generally by worthless, careless, and irresponsible publishers and distributors, who quickly reaped a golden harvest by way of cheaply produced but highly priced volumes smuggled into the country, or otherwise circulated. The obscenity laws, in fact, created a demand, and very clearly encouraged a supply, of anything which might be classed within the zone of 'Forbidden Literature'. Just as the 'Prohibition' laws of America had encouraged the illicit distillation of 'hooch', gangsterism and the speak-easy racket, together with the smuggling of genuine liquor in brands good, bad, and indifferent.

* The following is a small sample of the misprints which appear throughout this shoddy 'Parisiennes' paraphrase. All appear on page 60: ffoman (i.e. woman), ffich (which), ffith (with), trubles (troubles), nothin (nothing), nevr (never), shart (short), ffay (way), sighted (sighed).

It seems, however, that the common-sense of our new laws, backed by the serious and academic discussion of such literature by critics and scholars alike, may do much to foster an intelligent, healthy, and cathartic interest in the erotic, as opposed to the comparatively widespread and secret imbibing of a vast mass of indiscriminate and clandestine smut. The open method of publication encourages taste and discrimination on the part of the reader. The underground method encourages nothing but curiosity and a compulsive lust for the forbidden, as well as the dissemination of much specially-written trash which has no claim whatever to distinction, literary, scientific, or otherwise.

3. The Matter and the Manner

THE CONTENTS OF NEFZAWI'S book are similar to those of the *Kama Sutra*, the *Ananga Ranga*, and an Arabic treatise known as *The Book of Exposition in the Science of Coition*. All of them discuss human sexual activity reverentially, without lubricity, and consider it to be a natural and necessary facet in the divine design. Nefzawi, in particular, might aptly be described as an Arabic predecessor of the distinguished Dutch gynaecologist, Van de Velde, whose text-book on sexual technique, *Ideal Marriage*, has now become one of the standard medical manuals of the West. The scope of his work, however, is wider, for besides treating frankly of sexual physiology, coital technique, and the various postures, he deals at considerable length with aphrodisiacs,* stimulant foods, medicines, and the types of men and women (divided and subdivided according to temperament and physique) who are to be desired. It is interesting to note that the criteria of feminine seductiveness described by the Shaykh coincides almost entirely with that of the Old Testament, the attractiveness of whose women seems to have been determined by such characteristics as a white skin, scarlet

---

* Quite a number of the Oriental herbs, juices, berries, animal secretions, and foodstuffs prescribed in these aphrodisiac remedies are difficult to obtain in the Occident.

lips, firm breasts, rounded thighs, broad hips, a long neck, shining dark eyes, black hair or hair dyed with Henna, and a healthy
erect posture.

The erotic atmosphere of the *Garden* is, in fact, that of *The
Song of Solomon* – or even that of *The Ecstasy* of Donne. It is
the pure, free, non-obsessional, non-guilt-laden eroticism of the
Greeks or the Elizabethans.

One curious chapter, which has its Renaissance counterpart
in the immortal *Gargantua et Pantagruel* of Rabelais, lists an
incredibly large number of interesting synonyms for the male
member.* Another – and not the least fascinating – deals with
the interpretation of dreams. Some of its conclusions, in the
light of modern knowledge, are merely amusing; others, however, according to one commentator, coincide surprisingly with
Freudian psychology.†

Throughout, the *Garden* is punctuated with legends, folk-
tales, and anecdotes, illustrative of the subject matter of the text
proper. One sequence of these narrative interpolations is devoted to the deceits and treacheries of women in matters of love.
In fact the tales and stories, on the whole, are remarkably
similar in content, conception, and style, to many of those in
the infinitely more voluminous *Arabian Nights* – and probably
owe their origin to similar sources.

There is also a discussion regarding amatory excess, the

---

* A good French edition of Rabelais is that by C. Marty-Laveaux (1868-
1903, in six volumes). The Urquhart-Motteux translation remains standard,
and is still obtainable in the Everyman edition (two volumes.). Excellent
modern translations are : *The Histories of Gargantua and Pantagruel* . . .
Translated and with an Introduction by J. M. Cohen, Harmondsworth,
Penguin Books, 1955 (and reprints); and *The Complete Works of Rabelais*
. . . in the modern translation of Jacques Le Clerq. New York, Random
House (Modern Library Giant), 1944, etc. Both the ancient Latin, and the
modern French languages (in argot), provide a rich vocabulary of erotic
synonyms.

† It would be interesting to make a detailed comparison and study of
the dream interpretations of old writers, such as Nefzawi, the interpretations as found throughout the folk-lore of the world and in the writings
of the occultists, and then to compare these with the findings of Freud,
Stekel, and Havelock Ellis, etc.

Introduction 29

dangers attendant thereon, and the means to be employed in combating the ills which may arise from coition. These include eating slowly, masticating thoroughly, and the avoidance of drinking quantities of liquid immediately after a meal – advice which might be considered sound in every circumstance of life. A warning is also given as to the avoidance of drugs and the folly of over-medication.

As regards love-play, coital posture and technique, the *Garden* offers some interesting ethnological variations and modifications – as do the *Kama Sutra*, and other Oriental manuals.* In this connection some remarks of Kinsey are particularly pertinent in the present context:

> Most persons will be surprised to learn that positions in intercourse are as much a product of human cultures as languages and clothing, and that the common English-American position is rare in some other cultures. Among the several thousand portrayals of human coitus in the art left by ancient civilisations, there is hardly a single portrayal of the English-American position. It will be recalled that Malinowski† records the nearly universal use of a totally different position among the Trobrianders in the Southwestern Pacific; and he notes that caricatures of the English-American position are performed around the communal campfires, to the great amusement of the natives who refer to the position as the 'missionary position'.
>
> The origin of our present custom is involved in early and later Church history, and needs clarification before it can be presented with any authority; but certain it is that there was a time in the history of the Christian Church when the utilisation of any other except the present-day position was made a matter for confession. What has been taken to be a question of biologic normality proves, once again, to be a matter of cultural development.‡

* Not to mention the literature of Greece, Rome (and the art of those civilisations), the literature of the Europe of the Renaissance, of the eighteenth century, and the sexo-medical writings of our own day.

† Malinowski: *The Sexual Life of Savages* . . . with a Preface by Havelock Ellis. London, Routledge, 1932 (American edition: New York, Halcyon House, 1929).

‡ Kinsey, *Sexual Behaviour in the Human Male*, Philadelphia, W. B. Saunders, 1948 (pages 373-374).

Magnificent reproductions (many in full and accurate colour) of the erotic art of ancient civilisations are to be found in the following three volumes published at Paris and Geneva by Nagel, and at London by Skilton. The dates of publication are given in brackets after the title, and

The traditional sexual education of the Orient aims, of course, at the increase and prolongation of pleasure, and is designed to assist both men and women to avoid monotony and satiety – so that each of the partners in a union may live through many years together as though each were always young. The Arab, moreover, has cultivated the special art of delaying the male orgasm. This practice is known as *Imsák*, and is described by Sir Richard Burton in one of the footnotes to his *Arabian Nights* (Vol. v, page 76): '. . . The essence of the retaining art is to avoid over-tension of the muscles and to pre-occupy the brain . . . Europeans ignoring the science are contemptuously compared with village-cocks by Hindu women. . .'*

The aim of these ancient sex manuals is, primarily, the inculcation of a healthy sexual attitude and practice, as well as the promotion of happy and contented marriages. And the pages of Nefzawi are best understood against the background of Mohammedan marriage and its customs. Space will not permit the examination of this topic in the present Introduction, but a large variety of informative works are available for the interested reader.† The Christian and Islamic approaches to marriage are, of course, somewhat different, and have recently briefly been summed up by a modern commentator on the *Koran*: 'For Christianity, celibacy is the strictest religious ideal; even monogamy is a concession to human nature. For Mussulmans

the volumes, in large format, deal respectively with India, Rome, and Greece: *Kama Kala* (1958), *Roma Amor* (1961), and *Eros Kalos* (1962). The text to the first volume is by the distinguished art historian, Mulk Raj Anand, and those to the volumes on Greece and Rome are by Professor Jean Marcadé of the University of Bordeaux.

* The *Ananga Ranga* (Kama Shastra Society edition, page 41) gives innumerable recipes for retarding the male orgasm – and many, also, for hastening that of the female.

† For the general reader the following are useful: Lane's *Modern Egyptians* (Everyman Library, 1936 etc.); Burton's *Pilgrimage* (two vols., London, G. Bell & Sons, 1898, 1926, etc); Gérard de Nerval: *The Women of Cairo* (a translation by Conrad Elphinstone of *Voyage en Orient*, published at Paris by Charpentier in 1851), London, Routledge, 1929 (two vols.). Especially interesting is: George Allgrove's *Love in the East*, London, Anthony Gibbs & Phillips, 1962.

the ideal is monogamy, the concession to human nature is polygamy.'*

The mention of marriage brings us naturally to the position of women in the Arabia of *The Perfumed Garden*. Burton himself has described their situation from his own first-hand knowledge:

> The next point I propose to consider is the position of womanhood . . . so curiously at variance with the stock ideas concerning the Moslem home and domestic policy still prevalent, not only in England, but throughout Europe. Many readers . . . have remarked to me with much astonishment that they find the female characters more remarkable for decision, action, and manliness than the male; and are wonderstruck by their masterful attitude and the supreme influence they exert upon public and private life.
>
> I have glanced at the subject of the sex in Al-Islam to such an extent throughout my notes† that little remains here to be added. Women, all over the world, are what men make them; and the main charm of Amazonian fiction is to see how they live and move and have their being without any masculine guidance. But it is the old evernew fable.
>
> 'Who drew the Lion vanquished? 'Twas a man!'
>
> The books of the Ancients, written at that stage of civilisation when the sexes are at civil war, make women even more than in real life the creatures of their masters: hence from the dawn of literature to the present day the sex has been the subject of disappointed abuse, and eulogy almost as unmerited . . .
>
> The legal status of womankind in Al-Islam is exceptionally high, a fact of which Europe has often been assured, although the truth has not even yet penetrated into the popular brain. Nearly a century ago one Mirza Abú Tálib Khán, an Amildár or revenue collector, after living two years in London, wrote an 'apology' for, or rather a vindication of his countrywomen which is still worth reading and quoting.‡ Nations are but superficial judges of one another: where customs differ they often remark only the salient points which, when examined, prove to be of minor importance. Europeans seeing and hearing that women in the East are 'cloistered'; that wives may not walk out with their husbands and cannot accompany them to 'balls and parties'; moreover, that they are always liable, like the ancient Hebrew, to the mortification of the 'sister-wife', have most ignorantly

* Mohammed M. Pickthall: *The Meaning of the Glorious Koran*. New York, 1954 (pages 405-6).

† Burton refers here to the voluminous footnotes to his translation of the *Arabian Nights*.

‡ A note informs us that this 'apology' was translated into English and printed in the *Asiatic Annual Register* for 1801 (pages 100-7) under the title of: *On the Vindication of the Liberties of the Asiatic Women*.

determined that they are mere serviles and that their lives are not worth living. Indeed a learned lady, Miss Martineau, once visiting a Harem, went into ecstasies of pity and sorrow because the poor things knew nothing of – say trigonometry and the use of the globes. Sonnini thought otherwise, and my experience, like that of all old dwellers in the East, is directly opposed to this conclusion . . .

Lastly, Moslems and Easterns in general study and intelligently study the art and mystery of satisfying the physical woman. In my Foreword* I have noticed among barbarians the system of 'making men' (and women), that is of teaching lads first arrived at puberty the nice conduct of the *instrumentum paratum plantandis civibus;* a branch of the knowledge-tree which our modern education grossly neglects, thereby entailing untold miseries upon individuals, families and generations. The mock virtue, the most immodest modesty of England and the United States in the Nineteenth century, pronounces the subject foul and fulsome: 'Society' sickens at all details; and hence it is said abroad that the English have the finest women in Europe and least know how to use them. Throughout the East such studies are aided by a long series of volumes, many of them written by learned physiologists, by men of social standing, and by religious dignitaries in high office. The Egyptians especially delight in aphrodisiac literature treating, as the Turks say, *de la partie au-dessous de la taille* . . . The pudibund Lane† makes allusion to and quotes (*Arabian Nights*, i, 216) one of the most outspoken, a 4to of 464 pages, called the *Halbat al-Kumayt* or *Race-Course of the Bay Horse,* a poetical and horsey term for grape-wine. Attributed by D'Herbelot to the Kazi Shams al-Din Mohammed, it is wholly upon the subject of wassail and women . . . Even the divine and historian Jalal al-Din al-Siyuti is credited with having written, though the authorship is much disputed, a work entitled, *Kitáb al-Izáh fi'ilm al-Nikáh – The Book of Exposition in the Science of Coition;‡* my copy, a lithograph of 33 pages, undated, but

* The Foreword to the *Arabian Nights,* vol. one.
† E. W. Lane, translator of a mutilated and bowdlerised version of the *Arabian Nights* (three vols. London, 1840. A modern reprint in one omnibus volume on thin paper – with the valuable notes on Arab customs etc. – was published at New York, Tudor Publishing Co., 1927). Lane's incomplete version of the *Nights* (meticulously expurgated by him) was based on the Bulak edition of the Arabic text. Burton followed the text of the edition of Macnaghten (1839-42), referring also to other editions.
‡ Translated into English and issued in a limited edition as follows: *The Book of Exposition (Secrets of Oriental Sexuology): Kitab al-Izah fi'ilm al-Nikah b-it-Tamam w-al-Kamal.* Literally translated from the Arabic by an English Bohemian, with Translator's Foreword, Numerous Important Notes Illustrating the Text, and Several Interesting Appendices. Aden, Privately Printed, MDCCC. *All Rights Reserved.* (Actually printed at Paris by Charles Carrington in 1900). The volume contains an interesting essay on 'Copulation and its Ethnical Variations'.

evidently Cairene, begins with exclaiming 'Alhamdolillah – Laud to
the Lord who adorned the virginal bosom with breasts and who made
the thighs of women anvils for the spear-handles of men !' To the same
amiable theologian are also ascribed the *Kitáb Nawázir al-Ayk fí al-
Nayk – Green Splendours of the Copse in Copulation,* an abstract of
the *Kitáb al-Wisháh fí fawáid al-Nikáh – Book of the Zone on Coition-
boon.*

Burton then quotes the titles of seven erotic manuals which
are listed on the second page of the Kitáb Rujú'a al-Shaykh ila
Sabáh fi'l-Kuwwat al-Báh – *The Book of Age-rejuvenescence in
the Power of Concupiscence,** a work by Ahmad bin Sulayman,
surnamed Ibn Kamál Pasha. These are :

1. Kitáb al-Báh by Al-Nahli
2. Kitáb al 'Ars wa al-'Aráis (*Book of the Bridal and the
   Brides*) by Al-Jáhiz
3. Kitáb al-Kiyán (*The Maiden's Book*) by Ibn Hájib al-Nu'mán
4. Kitáb al-Izáh fí asrár al-Nikáh (*Book of the Exposition on
   the Mysteries of Married Fruition*)
5. Kitáb Jámi' al-Lizzah (*The Compendium of Pleasure*) by
   Ibn Samsamani
6. Kitáb Barján (Yarján?) wa Janáhib
7. Kitáb al-Munákakah wa al-Mufátaha fí Asnáf al-Jimá' wa
   Alátih (*Book of Carnal Copulation and the Initiation into
   the modes of Coition and its Instrumentation*) by Aziz
   al-Din al-Masíhí

He then continues :

It must not be supposed that such literature is purely and simply
aphrodisiacal. The learned Sprenger,† a physician as well as an Arabist,
says (Al-Mas'údi, page 384) of a tractate by the celebrated Rhazes in

* Translated into English as : *The Old Man Young Again ... With ...*
numerous important Notes illustrating the text, and an Excursus on the
History, Nature and Uses of Aphrodisiacs. Two volumes. Paris, Charles
Carrington, 1898 – the edition was limited to 500 sets.
† Aloys Sprenger (1813-93) is meant here. He was an Austrian Orient-
alist, born at Nassereit in the Tyrol. In 1838 he became a naturalised
British subject. After acting as principal of a Mohammedan college at
Delhi he held other positions of importance in India, later becoming pro-
fessor of Oriental languages at Bern (1858). He edited many editions of
Persian and Arabian classics.

the Leyden Library: 'The number of curious observations, the correct
and practical ideas and the novelty of the notions of Eastern nations
on these subjects, which are contained in this book, render it one of
the most important productions of the medical literature of the Arabs.'
I can conscientiously recommend to the Anthropologist a study of
the '*Kutub al-Báh*.'*

Having looked at the matter of the book before the reader, it
now remains to glance at the manner; and so much of what
Burton has said concerning his *Arabian Nights* seems pertinent
to his translation of *The Perfumed Garden*, that we cannot do
better than quote once more from his *Terminal Essay* to that
work:

> Readers . . . will probably agree with me that the naïve indecencies of
> the text are rather *gaudisserie* than prurience; and, when delivered with
> mirth and humour, they are rather the 'excrements of wit' than designed
> for debauching the mind. Crude . . . with infantile plainness, . . . they
> cannot be accused of corrupting suggestiveness or subtle insinuation
> of vicious sentiment. Theirs is a coarseness of language, not of idea;
> they are not depraved; and the pure and perfect naturalness of their
> nudity seems almost to purify it, showing that the matter is rather
> of manners than of morals. Such, throughout the East, is the language
> of every man, woman, and child, from prince to peasant, from matron
> to prostitute: all are, as the naïve French traveller said of the Japanese:
> '*si grossiers qu'ils ne sçavant nommer les choses que par leur nom.*' This
> primitive stage of language sufficed to draw from Lane and Burkhardt
> strictures upon the 'most immodest freedom of conversation in Egypt,'
> where, as all the world over, there are three several stages for names of
> things and acts sensual . . . And let me observe that the highest civili-
> sation is now returning to the language of nature. In *La Glu* of M. J.
> Richepin, a triumph of the realistic school, we find such 'archaic'
> expressions as *la petée, putain, foutue à la six-quatre-dix, un facétieuse
> pétarade, tu t'es foutue de*, etc., *Eh vilain bougre!* and so forth. To those
> critics who complain of these raw vulgarisms and puerile indecencies
> . . . I can reply only by quoting the words said to have been said by
> Dr. Johnson to the lady who complained of the naughty words in his
> dictionary – 'Madam, you must have been looking for them!'†

* *Báh* is the popular term for the amatory appetite; thus *Kutub al-Báh*
are books or manuals dealing with erotic technique. The quotations above
on pages 31-4, are all from the section headed *Woman*, in Burton's long
Terminal Essay to the *Arabian Nights* (volume ten, pages 192-202).

† Burton, *Arabian Nights* (*Terminal Essay*), vol. ten, pages 203-5. In
a footnote to his *Pilgrimage* (London, Bell, 1898, 1926, vol. two, page 347)
Burton also remarks that the Moslems 'are disposed to be facetious on
serious subjects'.

What Burton says above regarding the wit, humour, and candour of the Arab, applies, of course, much more particularly to the illustrative stories and anecdotes interpolated into *The Perfumed Garden*, than to the text proper of the manual itself. And after all, this is wit and candour of precisely the same kind as that employed by the great Italian and French storytellers of the Renaissance – by Boccaccio in his *Decameron*, by Straparola in his *Piacevolissime Notti* (particularly the 'riddles' in verse which terminate each tale),* by Basile in his *Pentamerone* (also translated by Burton), by the author (or authors) of the inimitable *Cent Nouvelles Nouvelles*; and, above all, by that towering genius of healthy good humour, François Rabelais himself. The crudity – and commonsense – of Rabelais, like that of the Arab, was the result of living close to nature. As J. M. Cohen has said in the Introduction to his excellent modern translation of Rabelais, the French author related his material, even his wildest fancies, 'only to the three constants of this life : birth, copulation, and death, which he saw in their crudest physical terms. There was in the mind of this loose-living monk no twentieth-century conflict between the two sides of his nature, the scholar's and the peasant's. They played into one another's hands. Nor was he conscious of any inconsistency between his professed beliefs and the often pagan workings of his imagination. . .'†

Moreover, despite his levity, there are passages in Rabelais which indicate a considerable profundity of religious feeling, and an attitude of humble faith which the world might do well to recapture today. I speak, for instance, of the pages on prayer included in the *Prologue* to his *Fourth Book*.‡

* There is a complete English translation by W. G. Waters : *The Nights of Straparola*, . . . Illustrated by E. R. Hughes, A.R.W.S. Two vols. London, Lawrence & Bullen, 1894. Reprinted by Carrington (two vols.), Paris, 1906, in an edition of 1,000 sets with (different) hand-coloured plates. Straparola lived between *c.* 1495 and *c.* 1557. His tales are noteworthy as the first modern European collection based almost entirely on folk-lore. For the original, a good edition is that by Rua (1899).

† *Gargantua & Pantagruel*, Trans. J. M. Cohen, Penguin Books, 1955 (page 17).

‡ Translation as above, pages 440-9 inclusive.

This, allowing for differences between cultural background, outlook, and tradition, is not at all unlike the attitude of Nefzawi and other Oriental writers. And the tone of reverence is perhaps most marked in the Hindu – the *Kama Sutra*, for example – and in the Moslem. In his Introduction Nefzawi immediately warns us that his book is not to be considered as either a lascivious or an obscene text, and that his motives are of the highest.

There is, in fact, a similar and sincere reverence between the opening passages of the *Arabian Nights*, *The Perfumed Garden*, and the first Sura of the *Koran*. I quote briefly from each:

> Praise be to Allah, the Beneficient King, the Creator of the Universe, Lord of the Three Worlds, Who set up the Firmanent without Pillars in its Stead, and Who stretched out the Earth even as a Bed... (Burton, *Nights*, vol. one, page 1).

> Praise be given to God, who has placed man's greatest pleasure in the natural parts of woman, and has destined the natural parts of man to afford the greatest enjoyment to woman. (Burton, *Garden*, page 1).

> *In the Name of God, the Compassionate, the Merciful*
> Praise be to God, Lord of the Worlds!
> The compassionate, the merciful!
> King on the day of reckoning!
> Thee *only* do we worship, and to Thee do we cry for help.
> (Rodwell, *Koran*, Everyman ed., page 28).

And however precise Nefzawi may be in his directions concerning coital technique, he frowned upon adultery, quoting in his text the sharp criticism of an unknown Arab poet regarding such behaviour:

'Certain it is, such conduct is not to be praised and honoured.'

A very obvious fact, but one which does not seem to have been thoroughly grasped by the West, is that the peoples of the Orient are much less sexually inhibited than we – but they are, at the same time, much more deeply religious in the truest sense. And they look upon love and sexual activity, not only as a natural and healthy and necessary part of life, but also as an art. Balzac, of all people, captured something of their spirit in the aphorisms scattered throughout his *Physiologie du Mariage*:

'Love is an art – the art of pleasing women.' Or again: 'One should never allow himself any pleasure with his wife unless he is first a master in the art of making her desire that same pleasure.' This is the basic attitude behind the Oriental approach towards matters of love and sex. Sex, in fact, is permitted by the Moslem religion, with polygamy (within certain specified limits) as something of a condescension to the nature of the human being. And sexual instruction for them, above all, aims at providing the soundest possible basis for successful marriage and family life.

Who, moreover, could better be qualified to translate the erotic treatises of such peoples than Sir Richard Burton, a man who had lived amongst them, who knew almost every shade of their thought, feeling, and habit, and who himself had adopted their way of life into the smallest detail. Distinguished as a soldier, as an explorer, and not least as a man of letters, and with the mastery of something like thirty-five languages to his credit, his achievement as a writer was little short of astonishing. His many published works cover everything from poetry and travel to scholarly translation; and he was a rare master in the art of annotation. Added to this he was gifted with an almost unique facility in the collection and classification of an incredible mass of obscure and fascinating facts and information, much of which was to be incorporated in the footnotes to his varied works.

It is in this last connection that the late J. S. Cotton was able to write of him: 'This, again, was but another facet of Burton's many-sided nature . . . His insatiable curiosity led him to explore almost every path of learning, especially the bypaths. The origins of civilisation, the hoary antiquity of Egypt, prehistoric connections between the East and the West, the ancient race of the Etruscans, the mysticism of the Sufis, the wanderings of the Gypsies, the colonial empire of the Portuguese – these were some of the matters that had a special fascination for him. His cast of mind was so original that not only did he never borrow from anyone else, but he was disposed to resent another's trespassing upon such subjects as he considered his own. But no man could be more cordial in his admiration of honest work done in bordering fields of learning. He was ever ready to assist, from the stores of his experience, young explorers and young scholars; . . . His virility stamped everything he said or wrote. His style was as characteristic as his handwriting . . . And, with Burton, the style was the man. No one could meet him without being convinced of his transparent sincerity. He concealed nothing; he boasted of nothing.'

This is a very accurate description of Burton the scholar, the man with an omnivorous appetite for painstaking research, for the discovery and sifting of little known but illuminating facts. It also indicates something of the vision of the man who assuredly would have agreed with Keyserling's statement that 'the erotic images of India never belonged to pornography, but to iconography.'

This mention of the word 'pornography' suggests a brief consideration of the term, together with its interpretation. Originally, and literally, it means any writing descriptive of the manners, behaviour and habits of whores (see the *Oxford Dictionary*). Currently, and generally, it has come to indicate a worthless species of aphrodisiac writing, without any literary, artistic, or scientific value. Such writing may, however, contrary to popular opinion – and this statement is based on qualified psychiatric opinion* – more often than not become a safety valve for antisocial tendencies, thus preventing the manifestation of overt delinquent conduct.

Drs. Eberhard and Phyllis Kronhausen, however, have recently distinguished between pornography (which they term 'hard core obscenity'), and another form of erotic writing which they describe (very precisely) as 'erotic realism'. Erotic realism involves a candid and honest description of the basic realities of life. Such description may be sexually stimulating, or it may be not,

* See Alec Craig, *The Banned Books of England*, London, Allen & Unwin, 1962, pages 212-13.

depending on the temperament, environment, and preferences (even the sense of humour) of the reader. But – and this is important – it is perfectly legitimate for a reader to respond to writing which may be classified under the heading of erotic realism; it is perfectly legitimate to be interested in it; and it is equally healthy and legitimate to derive instruction and enlightenment from it in one way or another, whether the work be fiction, poetry, or a scientific study.

The Kronhausens include in their category of erotic realism all the great literary classics such as Aretino, Poggio, Rabelais, Brantôme, Casanova, Restif, Pepys, Zola, Nabokov, Lawrence, and even Mark Twain's *Conversation at the Social Fireside* (a satire on the manners and morals of the Elizabethans). They also, and very justifiably, include the love manuals of the East (the *Kama Sutra, Ananga Ranga, Perfumed Garden,* and so on); and, by extension, we may further include the scientific sex manuals of our own day, including those studies which analyse numerous case histories.

It seems appropriate to conclude the present section of this Introduction by quoting a reflection from Craig's previously mentioned, and admirably documented book: 'Erotic realism reflects a basically healthy and therapeutic attitude to life, and its effects on the average person are generally beneficial.'

4.   The *Garden* and other Manuals

IN SO FAR AS manuals of sexual instruction are concerned, there seem to be, broadly speaking, three more or less clearly defined categories. The first of these is mainly geographical, and concerns itself with the literary productions of India, Arabia, Persia, etc. The second and third are geographical and historical, and concern themselves with a specific kind of European literature, roughly covering the periods from Ovid to the close of the eighteenth century, and from the emergence of scientific method in sexology up to its elaborate development at the present time. We shall deal with them, and describe their characteristics in that order:

The instructional manuals of Oriental erotology present love as, in a sense, a sacrament, and look upon the sexual act not only as a means to procreation, but also as a healthy (even a healing) pleasure.* On its highest and purest level they regard coition virtually, and sometimes literally, as an act of worship.† An Arab poet has ideally expressed the fundamental reverence underlying their attitude: 'Love enters in through the eyes, which are the doors of the spirit, and then diffuses himself throughout the whole of the soul.'

Thus, for the Oriental, orgasm symbolised the ecstasy of the soul possessed by, or in union with God, even though it yet remained imprisoned within the confines of the flesh. The intelligent Westerner can, in fact, learn much from a simultaneous

* Havelock Ellis, with a wisdom almost Oriental, realised the considerable importance of the non-procreative aspects of sex: 'The functions of sex on the psychic and erotic side are of far greater extension than any act of procreation, they may even exclude it altogether, and when we are concerned with the welfare of the individual human being we must enlarge our outlook and deepen our insight.' (*Little Essays of Love and Virtue* – see the essay entitled: *The Play-Function of Sex*. London, A. & C. Black, 1922; New York, Doubleday Doran, 1922; reprinted as a paper-back, under the new title of: *On Life & Sex*, New York, Mentor Books, 1957.) The essay referred to was also included in: McDermott: *The Sex Problem in Modern Society*, an anthology in the 'Modern Library' series, Random House, New York, 1931 (page 99). More recently Dr. Albert Ellis has said (*Art & Science of Love*, New York, Lyle Stuart, 1960, page 256): 'We know today, as the ancient Hebrews did not, that human sexuality is designed for fun and frolic, as well as for procreative ends. If non-procreative acts were deviated we would have to call millions of married individuals who use contraceptives . . . sex perverts.'

† More particularly in that form known as *Maithuna*. The indices to Mircea Eliade: *Yoga: Immortality & Freedom*, London, Routledge, 1958, together with the very full bibliography to this work, will supply useful information and references. The reader should also see the essay by Mulk Raj Anand, which prefaces *Kama Kala* (London, Skilton; Geneva, Nagel, 1958); the Introduction by K. M. Pannikar to W. G. Archer's edition of Burton's translation of the *Kama Sutra* (London, Allen & Unwin, 1963 – especially pages 74-5); and the various writings and commentaries on Tantrism of Sir John Woodroffe ('Arthur Avalon'). Aldous Huxley also has some interesting things to say, more or less in this connection, in the Appendix to his *Adonis and the Alphabet*, London, Chatto & Windus, 1956 (New York, Harper).

study of the religious volumes and the love-books of the East. Those who do so will discover that while we of the occident owe most of our religions and even our love rites to the East, the East, on the contrary, owes nothing to the West – excepting those double-edged and frequently more than dubious 'advantages' which it has only recently borrowed from our crassly material, cynical, technological, mechanised, industrial, publicity and status-symbol-conscious civilisation. It can be said that civilisation, and even religion, which have their well-springs in the East, have been largely taken over and not infrequently corrupted by the West . . .

Over and above the fundamental reverence inherent in Oriental sexuality, however, was the commonsense typified by Kalyana Malla, who wrote in his *Ananga Ranga*:

> The chief reason for the separation between the married couple, and the cause which drives the husband to the embraces of strange women, and the wife to the arms of strange men, is the want of varied pleasures, and the monotony which follows possession. There is no doubt about it . . . Fully understanding the way in which such quarrels arise, I have . . . shown how the husband, by varying the enjoyment of his wife, may live with her as with thirty-two different women, ever varying the enjoyment of her, and rendering satiety impossible . . .*

Here we have affectionate consideration together with a highly developed 'art of love', each based upon a reverence for religion, marriage, and family life. Sexual technique is encouraged as a natural means towards the happiness of the individual, the stability of the home, and, not least, the achievement of that union symbolic of the unity of the Divine. These, then, are the special and ideal characteristics of Oriental erotic treatises. That individuals and even groups, sometimes in quite considerable numbers, should fall short of the attainment of such ideals, is quite understandable. But at least the better way has clearly been delineated for them.

When, however, we turn to the second category of erotic

* Translated by Burton.

writing – that of Europe – which covers the period from the civilisation of ancient Rome down to approximately the close of the eighteenth century (allowing for a long blank during the dark ages of Medieval times, and completely ignoring the ethereal affectations of that literature representative of the knightly 'Courts of Love'), we find quite a different picture, and a totally different approach.

Taking Ovid as the supreme example of ancient Rome – and the prototype of what was to follow throughout the Renaissance and the eighteenth century – we find the sexual act, and even promiscuity, unashamedly extolled as pleasure for pleasure's sake. In the *Art of Love** there are neither moral nor religious considerations; nor are there any implications that sex may well partake of the quality of a sacrament; or that, properly understood and experienced, it may become a means of experiencing that symbolic ecstasy wherein duality becomes unity.† In reality Ovid's book is not a manual on the art of love, but a handbook on the technique of seduction and the selfish attainment of pleasure. He preaches illicit love, and teaches the superficial manners of the boudoir. His morals and aims, in fact, are simply those depicted in Schnitzler's cynical *La Ronde*.

This attitude is reflected in the erotic works of the Renaissance, and in such treatises on erotic technique as Chorier's *Dialogues of Luisa Sigea*,‡ originally printed at Lyons, about 1660. The same may be said of Friedrich-Karl Forberg's voluminous

---

* Dryden's translation is bawdy, and tends to misrepresent the original. A revised and corrected version of a good Elizabethan translation – that of Wolferston – is contained in the Everyman edition of *Ovid: Selected Works* (London & New York, 1939). J. Lewis May's prose version, originally published by The Bodley Head in 1925, has recently been reprinted as a paperback by Elek (Bestseller Library), London, 1959.

† The relation between religious and other forms of ecstasy, together with genuine ecstasy as an experience in sexual activity, have been discussed with lucidity and insight by Marghanita Laski in: *Ecstasy*, London, The Cresset Press, 1961 (pages 145-53).

‡ French translations were published by Liseux, Paris, in 1881 (incomplete) and 1882 (an absolutely complete version). The same publisher issued an English translation during 1890. All are extremely rare today.

commentary on the *Hermaphroditus* of Beccadelli, since printed separately under the title of *A Manual of Classical Erotology*.*

It is also the prevalent mood of Cleland's notorious *Fanny Hill* (a book, however, which contains brief moments of an almost idyllic charm, in those passages describing Fanny's genuine love for the young Charles – whom she eventually marries). And it reaches its climax towards the end of the eighteenth century, after a seemingly endless stream of ephemeral boudoir erotica, in the abominations of the Marquis de Sade, who not only systematically trampled on religion in his attempt to extend the frontiers of libertinage, but also extolled the insane delights of pain, torture, and every conceivable form of viciousness.†

The third of our literary categories emerged towards the dawn of the twentieth century, and concerns itself with scientific works written by scientific men, with a view to clarifying the problems of sex in Europe and America. Their aims were humanitarian in the truest sense of the term; and besides their more comprehensive and learned studies, they also began to produce, for general reading, volumes describing the anatomy and physiology of sex, and its psychology, including clearly formulated directions concerning sexual technique – or what one might more adequately describe as 'the mechanics of sex'.

Two of the most celebrated amongst such manuals are undoubtedly Th. Van de Velde's *Ideal Marriage* (translated from the Dutch, and published by Heinemann, London, 1929),‡ and

---

* The first edition, in Latin, was published at Coburg in 1824, under the title: *Antonii Panormitae Hermaphroditus; Primus in Germania Editit et Apophoreta Adjecit Frid. Carol. Forbergius. Coburgi, Sumtibus Museliorum.* (8vo). A Latin text and English translation of the commentary (i.e. *Apophoreta*) was issued in two vols., in an edition of 100 copies, privately, and with the antedate of 1884. It is rare.

† In the interminable volumes of *Justine* (1791). *La Nouvelle Justine* and *Juliette* (1797), and *Les 120 Journées de Sodome* (ed. Heine, 1930-35).

‡ Dr. Ludwig Lenz (*Discretion & Indiscretion*, New York, Cadillac, 1951, page 407) informs us that Van de Velde told him he had written *Ideal Marriage* after coming into contact with a marriage wrecked by lack of sexual enlightenment.

Eustace Chesser's even more popular *Love Without Fear* (London, 1940).

They lack the religious basis of the *Kama Sutra* and the *Garden*, are infinitely less complex and varied, but equally scientific in their approach, even if this, together with the terminology permitted in those days, is a little coldly clinical and chill. Their aims, once more, are similar to those of the Oriental authors: Instruction for the sake of the stability of marriage and the maintenance of psychologic health; instruction for the avoidance of neurosis and the procreation of healthy children; instruction for the promotion of a physical and emotional satisfaction with life, which will produce men and women fully and happily productive in the spheres of their employment, and in the upbringing of their children.

There can be no doubt that many of the innumerable authors of popular volumes of sex instruction owe at least a little of their systematology to the writings of Vatsyayana, Nefzawi, and Kalyana Malla. They likewise owe some of their information to the copious and profoundly informed annotations to Burton's *Nights*. And the most distinguished have clearly stated their references. Havelock Ellis, for example, refers to and quotes Nefzawi in his monumental *Studies in the Psychology of Sex*; Kinsey does likewise in his *Sexual Behaviour in the Human Female*; and Norman Himes also included *The Perfumed Garden* among the Arabic sources utilised when writing his unique *Medical History of Contraception*.* The list could be extended, but it seems a trifle unnecessary to state the obvious.

Too much, however, must not be expected from the reading, either of Oriental manuals of erotology, or of contemporary guides to sex-technique. These are mainly concerned with niceties

---

* *Medical History of Contraception* by Norman E. Himes, Ph.D. Medical Foreword by Robert Latou Dickinson, M.D., F.A.C.S. London, Allen & Unwin, 1936 (Baltimore, Williams & Wilkins Co., 1936). The English edition contains an additional Preface by Sir Humphrey Rolleston, Bt., G.C.V.O., K.C.B., F.R.C.P.I., etc. The volume was issued in conjunction with the National Committee on Maternal Health, Inc., and is the standard work on the subject. It occupies xxxii + 521 pages quarto.

in approach, and with the necessary details concerning the mechanics of love-play, intercourse, and coital posture.* Much more could undoubtedly be learned, concerning the art of attracting and seducing women, from the *Memoirs of Casanova* – or even, as has been suggested above, from Ovid's perennial handbook on *The Art of Love*. And while Vatsyayana, Nefzawi, and other Oriental writers respect, and are certainly considerate in their approach to women (much more so than many of our contemporary Europeans), one might possibly acquire more useful guidance in the art of respect for the fair sex from a study of the writings of Restif de la Bretonne,† than from any work specifically expounding the details of technique.

Nevertheless, with regard to this very important and practical aspect of love – so much ignored by the West – the Orientals have no peer. And Nefzawi is the classic Arab example. His work, in addition to its immediate aim, is also a valuable, if minor, compendium of relative folklore. But it is not – nor did he intend it to be – an easy pass-key to unlimited seduction or licence. This should become clear to the reader as he studies the text; though it is important that he should bear in mind the fact that Mohammedans are legally allowed a plurality of wives, not only by law, but by religion.

5. The Present Edition

THE PRESENT EDITION reproduces the full, complete, and unexpurgated text of the original Kama Shastra Society edition of *The Perfumed Garden*, with the exception that two short anec-

* These, of course vary (as Kinsey and others have pointed out), not only in number and manner, but also geographically and historically. Vatsyayana describes a greater number of postures than does Nefzawi; while Forberg, restricting himself to the positions assumed in ancient Greece and Rome, describes 90 (only 48, however, can be considered usual). Most modern medical treatises describe only 13, following Van de Velde. All other positions are merely slight variations of these.

† Particularly in his autobiography, *Monsieur Nicolas* (Paris, 1794-7). English edition, edited by Havelock Ellis: London, Rodker, 1930-1 (six vols.).

dotes, which have no genuine bearing on the main text, have been omitted. These are *The Story of the Man who was made a Cuckold by his Ass*, and *The Story of the Useless Precautions*. Both were placed in chapter eleven: *On the Deceits and Treacheries of Women*.

The first of these episodes, while typical of the Arab storyteller, is concerned with bestiality, and thus throws no light on the main subject of the book, which is human sexuality in its heterosexual form. Such tales are not uncommon in the East, and have their parallels in the literature of Greece and Rome (in *The Ass* of Lucius, and *The Golden Ass* of Apuleius, for example*), but might well offend the taste, even of many who widely accept the strange facts of comparative sexual behaviour.

The second episode relates, with crude humour, how a woman deceives her husband by engaging in coitus with her lover through a hole cut in a door. The same story reappears, considerably modified and transformed, and much more appropriately placed, in the pages of that great French classic, the *Cent Nouvelles Nouvelles* (of which there is an English translation by Robert B. Douglas, Paris, Carrington, no date [c. 1900])† A modified version also appears, under the title of: *One Does Not Think of Everything*, in the Second Book of the *Contes* of La Fontaine. The Arab tale, however, bears only the slightest relation to its context, and lacks the subtle delicacy and wit which distinguish its French descendants. The other stories in this section of the *Garden* illustrate much more pointedly the 'deceits and treacheries of women'. Therefore *The Story of the Useless Precautions* has been deleted.

* Robert Graves has made a fine English translation from Apuleius: *The Golden Ass* . . . Harmondsworth, Penguin Books (Series: 'Penguin Classics') 1950 (and reprints). The same translation was published in America by Farrar, Straus & Young, New York, 1951, and later as a paperback in Mentor Books.

† See the *Cent Nouvelles Nouvelles*, Story the Third (*The Search for the Ring*) Carrington edition, page 19. In this version the hole in the door has disappeared, but the woman explains her behaviour (as does her counterpart in Nefzawi) by saying that she has been searching for a lost jewel (in the one case a ring, in the other a trinket).

In his sixth chapter, *Concerning Everything that is Favourable to the Act of Coition,* Nefzawi describes the eleven coital positions in common use among the people of his time and country. He then mentions the numerous postures said to be in use in India, and continues to describe them in a series of comparatively short paragraphs. Four of these descriptions of 'Indian' postures have been omitted. Three are virtually impossible, and even dangerous. The fourth, besides being ungainly and awkward, is not one that would be likely to commend itself to men or women either of the Orient or the West.

Likewise four names for the sexual organ of the male, and five for the corresponding portion of the female anatomy, have been omitted from the long list of Arabic synonyms for the sexual parts of the two sexes. This has been done because it was felt that the particular examples were too coarsely humorous, in a sense not easily appreciated by the Western mind – and, in the case of the female, unpleasantly odoriferous. The very large remainder have been retained because of their interest for the scholar, the anthropologist, and other serious students.

The reader may rest assured that this deletion of a few very brief and unimportant references in no way injures the sense or the text of Nefzawi's book.

One interpolation has been made, in parenthesis, in the *Notes of the Translator respecting the Cheikh Nefzaoui* (on page 69 below). This is to the effect that the anecdote concerning bestiality has been omitted, and seemed essential if the remarks made here were to correspond with chapter eleven as now printed.

The French form of Arabic names and words has been retained, exactly as in Burton's original issue, even to the retention, in the text proper, of 'Nefzaoui' for Nefzawi. Burton's reason for employing these French forms, when he was perfectly capable of anglicizing the spelling, has already been suggested above, on page 19. The prejudiced (and most immoral) moral climate of his period obliged not a few of our best writers and scholars to employ strange subterfuges.

A number of new footnotes have been added to the text proper. These are distinguished from those of the original edition by initials enclosed in brackets, thus: (A.H.W.). An extension to an original note is indicated by a dash, preceding the extension; which, in its turn, is followed by the initials as above.

For the rest, all printer's errors have been corrected, together with a few obvious errors in punctuation, and some minor slips overlooked by the proof-readers of the Kama Shastra edition. Nevertheless, some occasional idiosyncrasies in punctuation and in the use of capitals, due partly to the period of the translation and partly to the habit of the translator, have been retained. For we are presenting Burton's classic translation in its original form, and not in a modernised version.

6.   Conclusion

IN CONCLUSION it might be profitable briefly to glance at the origins of that confusion of shame and filth which for centuries was so much associated in the Christian mind with sex and sexual activity. Such associations seem in no way to reflect the divine wisdom and wholesome teachings of Jesus, and have contributed immeasurably to the unutterable total of human misery and suffering. Sex must always be controlled, not only in the interests of society, but in those of the individual himself. Control, however, is a healthy thing. The bespattering of a God-given and natural function, so that it becomes associated with filth and foulness, is not – it is, on the contrary, a diabolical thing – and such a bespattering (which ultimately becomes a permeation) may well be one of the gravest sins against the Divinity of God Himself. Such are the sentiments which are making themselves felt in the new religious revival, and which are finding expression through the unofficial, but considered (and inspired) opinions of the new Cambridge theologians headed by Dr. A. R. Vidler, and others of like mind and enlightenment.*

* See, particularly: *Soundings: Essays Concerning Christian Understanding.* Cambridge, University Press, 1962; and the very Christian *Objec-*

With these thoughts in mind, let us then consider some penetrating observations by Havelock Ellis, first published towards the close of the last century :

> Something even stronger than theology or metaphysics has served to cut us off from the spirit of Jesus, and that is the spirit of Paul, certainly the real founder of 'Christianity', as we know it, for Jerome, Augustine, Luther, were all the children of Paul, and in no respect the children of Jesus. That marvellous little Jew painted in its main outlines the picture of Christianity which in the theatre of this world has for so many centuries shut us off from Jesus. Impelled by the intense and concentrated energy of his twisted suffering nature, Paul brought 'moral force' into our western world, and after it that infinite procession of hypocrisies and cruelties and artificialities which still trains loathsomely across the scene of civilised life. Jesus may have been a visionary, but his visions were in divine harmony with the course of nature, with the wine and the bread of life, with children and with flowers. We may be very sure that Paul never considered the lilies, or found benediction with children. He trampled on nature when it

tions to *Christian Belief*, London, Constable, 1963. Both are edited by A. R. Vidler, Dean of King's College, Cambridge. Special attention should be given to the essays in each volume by H. A. Williams, M.A., Fellow and Dean of Trinity College, Cambridge. *Honest to God* by John Robinson, the Bishop of Woolwich (London, SCM Press Ltd., 1963) also provides much food for thought, and does not seem to me to be at all out of line with the beliefs of the great Christian mystics. One thing is certain – the Bishop's religion is neither amoral nor Godless, despite what some critics have said. On the contrary, he seems to further the vision of God at work in the depths of human life, and in the depths of the individual – the One ever-present in the many.

All these works deal to some extent with sex and morality, but the most significant and practical contribution ever presented by Christians towards the healthy understanding of all aspects of sex (including homosexuality) is the sane, balanced, and informed essay by a group of Quakers, humbly conceived and written in the spirit of true Christianity: *Towards a Quaker View of Sex* . . . Edited by Alastair Heron, London, Friends House, Euston Road, N.W.1., 1963. It is the joint work of a distinguished group of men and women, many of them Elders in the Society of Friends, and includes Kenneth C. Barnes, B.Sc., Anna M. Bidder, M.A., Ph.D. of Cambridge University, Richard Fox, M.B., B.S., M.R.C.P., D.P.M., and Alastair Heron, M.Sc., Ph.D., Fellow of the British Psychological Society.

The reader should also see: *A Religious Outlook for Modern Man* by Raynor C. Johnson, M.A., Ph.D., D.Sc. (With a Foreword by Leslie Weatherhead, C.B.E., M.A., D.D., etc.), London, Hodder & Stoughton, 1963. Chapter 9 offers some very stimulating thought (pages 117-25), and Johnson's remarks on 'The Nature of Sin' (pages 84-6) are worthy of attention. The volume itself (as are Johnson's previous books) is a work of considerable importance.

D

came in his way, and for the rest never saw it. He was not, as Festus thought, a madman, but whether or not, as his experiences seem to indicate, he was a victim to the 'sacred disease' of epilepsy, concerning his profoundly neurotic temperament there can be no manner of question . . .

Well-nigh everything that has ever been evil in Christianity, its temporal power, its accursed intolerance, its contempt for reason, for beautiful living, for every sweet and sunny and simple aspect of the world – all that is involved in the awful conception of 'moral force' – flows directly from Paul. What eternal torture could be adequate for so monstrous an offender? And yet, when you think of the potent personality concentrated in this morbid man, of his courage, of the intolerance that he wreaked on himself, the flashes of divine insight in his restless and turbulent spirit, of the humility of the neuropath who desired to be 'altogether mad', the pathos of it all, indignation falls silent. What can be said?

Thus Paul and not Peter was the rock on which the Church was built, and whatever virtues the Church may have possessed have not been the virtues of Jesus but the quite other virtues of Paul.*

St. Paul, as is well enough known, declared that it is better to marry than to burn with lust. This, however, was little more than a grudging concession to what he firmly believed the frailties of human nature, and it tended to contribute towards the idea that even in marriage there should be as little sexual intercourse as possible, and then only for the purposes of procreation.

Some of the early Fathers of the Church, however, were not so narrow-minded as St. Paul; and, whilst opposed to the spectacle of the naked human body – for their position was based upon a revolt against that paganism which had cultivated the body – there is evidence that they did not consider any sexual intercourse between married couples as sinful, whether for procreative ends or not. Indeed some of them, especially of the Eastern Church, having come under the healthy influence of Greek thought, gave expression to views on the subjects of nature, sex, and the body, of an order which might well have received a commendatory nod from Whitman or Goethe.

Ellis, elsewhere, points out that not all the Christian Fathers

* See the essay, *St. Francis & Others*, in *Affirmations*, London, Walter Scott, 1898. Reprinted by Constable, 1915-29 (pages 213-4) also reprinted in the Everyman *Selected Essays of Havelock Ellis*, 1936, (and reprints).

README9

were of the opinion of Paul, that not all of them necessarily associated the body or sex with sin and shame:

> Clement of Alexandria . . . protested, for instance, against that prudery which, as the sun of the classic world set, had begun to over-shadow life. 'We should not be ashamed to name,' he declared, 'what God has not been ashamed to create.' It was a memorable declaration because, while it accepted the old classic feeling of no shame in the presence of nature, it put that feeling on a new and religious basis harmonious to Christianity. Throughout, though not always quite consistently, Clement defends the body and the functions of sex against those who treated them with contempt. And as the cause of sex is the cause of women he always strongly asserts the dignity of women, and also proclaims the holiness of marriage, a state which he sometimes places above that of virginity.
>
> Unfortunately, it must be said, St. Augustine – another North African, but of Roman Carthage and not of Greek Alexandria – thought that he had a convincing answer to the kind of argument which Clement presented, and so great was the force of his passionate and potent genius that he was able in the end to make his answer prevail . . .
>
> Alike in the Eastern and Western Churches, however, both before and after Augustine, though not so often after, great Fathers and teachers have uttered opinions which recall those of Clement rather than of Augustine . . .*

Some of our progressive contemporary clergymen, realising the general healthiness of Clement's views, have even suggested his inclusion in the Lectionary, or Table of Lessons, of our Churches.†

Nevertheless, the attitudes of Clement and others among the early Fathers, whilst presenting affiliations with the thought of the philosophers and writers of ancient Greece and the extensive world of the Orient, never reached that point attained in Oriental

* Havelock Ellis: *Studies in the Psychology of Sex (Sex in Relation to Society)*. Vol. six in the F. A. Davis, Philadelphia, edition of 1906, pages 125-7; in the Random House, New York, reprint of 1936, see pages 125-7 of vol. four. Ellis's quotation is from the *Paedagogus* of Clement of Alexandria (lib. ii, cap. X). I think he is quoting from the translation which appeared in *The Ante-Nicene Fathers* (1885), translated by Roberts, Donaldson, and Coxe, but, as I no longer have a copy, I cannot be certain.

† *The Guardian* for the 10th May, 1963, reports that the Rev. J. C. Wansey, Rector of Woodford, suggested that the Lectionary might include some of the early Fathers. The same view seemed to be held by the Rev. D. F. Strudwick, from Southwark, who held that St. Clement was a good candidate for the same. The report is interesting, and should be read in its entirety.

art and writing, where the feeling for the human extends almost
to the sacred heights of transfiguration, banishing every vestige
of the idea of shame. And for the Oriental, in life, in literature,
as in art, the act of love is expressed with an entire abandon, a
complete and wholesome joy; and is accepted as presenting, in its
fundamental essence, something of the activity of the Divine
itself. For which reasons, as has been said, Islam in general looks
upon chastity not as an ideal, but as an unfortunate accident.

While there have always been individual Christian men and
women, laymen, as well as clergymen and saints, for whom
sexual activity has been an expression of the Gospel of Love
(and in this context we should perhaps rather speak of 'sexual
relatedness' than of sexual 'relationships'), the Christian Church,
throughout the period of the Middle Ages and the rise of Calvin-
ism, right down to our own times, passed through a dark and
terrible period in its approach to, and interpretation of, the problems of human love, sex, and sexual morality. The horror was
even increased by uncountable numbers of fanatical and over-
zealous laymen who considerably exaggerated the teachings of
the Church upon the subject. There were, however, gleams of
light here and there, for during the seventeenth century, Jeremy
Taylor, a married clergyman in the Church of England, published
his *Holy Living*, wherein he described coitus as an experience 'to
lighten the cares and sadnesses of household affairs, and to endear
each other.' The Rev. Dr. Sherwin Bailey, commenting on this,
writes: 'Taylor maintains that marriage is the queen of friend-
ships, and husband and wife are the best of all friends; the love
that binds them together is a "union of all things excellent": it
contains in it proportion and satisfaction and rest and confidence.'*

---

* See *Towards a Quaker view of Sex*, London, 1963, page 38, where Dr.
Bailey, speaking of earlier centuries, is quoted as saying: '. . . the general
impression left by the Church's teaching upon simple and unlearned
people can only have been that the physical relationship of the sexes was
regarded by religion as unworthy, if not as shameless and obscene . . . and
we can only guess at the psychological disturbances and conflicts which
it has produced in the lives of individuals.'

It is only in recent times, however, that such enlightenment has found anything like frequent and open expression. The tentative conclusions of the Quaker group, together with the essays and lectures of the new Cambridge theologians, seem, nevertheless, to indicate that we are very belatedly approaching something analogous to the healthy and open attitude of the Orientals regarding these vital matters.

The wife of a Newark vicar has even suggested, quite recently – and with, I feel, a remarkable understanding of the situation – that the Church of England should publish a text-book on love-making. Reporting on this, *The Guardian* (30th May, 1963) says: 'Writing in her husband's parish magazine, she said many wives had neglected to learn to make love skilfully and asked: "Is it time for the Church to write a handbook of Christian marriage which includes a section on learning the arts of love?" '*

In the popular mind sexual activity (or desire) and lust are not infrequently looked upon, uncritically, as interchangeable terms. In his long and invaluable essay on *Theology and Self-Awareness,*† the Rev. H. A. Williams has cast interesting new light on the interpretation of the term 'lust'. He points out that, for each of us, most of our true self, and much of our real value, remains hidden from us, largely within the deep confines of the sub-conscious and the unconscious. And then he goes on to say:

> Lust is often understood as sheer physical appetite. But this is not so. Animals do not lust after each other, and, among people, there can be overwhelming physical pleasure without lust. Lust arises because it is impossible for me to live without a sense of my own value. Such a sense of my own value *is* living. Without it, I cannot live. But to

* Rainbow Records have recently published a gramophone record setting out in simple language the facts of life for children. It is entitled: *The Wonderful Story of How You Were Born,* and its publicity quotes tributes from the Archbishop of York and the Roman Catholic Archbishop of Liverpool. The narration is by Robert Leigh, author of books for children. See *The Guardian,* 7th June, 1963.

† In *Soundings,* edited by A. R. Vidler, Cambridge University Press, 1962, page 88, etc., Williams draws attention to the brilliant depiction of lust in the character of Catherine Earnshaw in *Wuthering Heights,* pointing out that in terms of the story there was no physical intimacy.

the degree in which I am unaware of myself, to that degree I shall be incapable of realizing my own value . . . Hence the value which I cannot give myself from my own being, I try to steal for myself from somebody else. This attempt to snatch value for myself from somebody else is the essence of lust, and it is in the cause of this enterprise that the physical appetites are conscripted. It is mistaken to say that those appetites are in control. On the contrary they are under control, and what controls them is the me, unaware of what he is . . . and therefore desperately seeking value for himself from somebody else. It is in this way that the sinful soul (that is, the person unaware of his potential) makes the body corrupt.

In the same essay, with profoundly Christian perception and feeling, Williams draws attention to the very popular Greek film, *Never on Sunday*, and points out that it was concerned with a prostitute in the Piraeus. A young sailor picks her up, and she takes him back to her room:

In her room he becomes afraid, nervous, and on edge. This is not because he thinks he is embarking on something wicked, but because he distrusts his capacity for physical union. He is prey to destructive doubts about himself, not to moral scruples. The prostitute gives herself to him in such a way that he acquires confidence and self-respect. He goes away a deeper fuller person than he came in. What is seen is an act of charity which proclaims the glory of God. The man is now equipped as he was not before. Can Christians possibly say that devils were cast out of him by Beelzebub the Prince of the devils? . . .*

This, in essence, is the kind of blessing which writings like those of Nefzawi, Vatsyayana, Kalyana Malla, and modern medical authorities such as Van de Velde, rightly used, confer upon their readers. To wit, the dispersal of the fogs of ignorance, the imparting of a sound technique accompanied by a healthy mental attitude, and the inculcation of a confidence productive both of happiness and (for their respective religions) self-respect.

And it is thanks to the labours and learning of Sir Richard Burton that the *Kama Sutra*, the *Ananga Ranga*, and *The Perfumed Garden*, have become, for the West, beacons shining from the past and illuminating the future – a guiding light which can

* *Soundings*, pages 81-2. This very important essay should be read in its entirety (it occupies pages 69-101 of the volume); as also should Williams's essay *Psychological Objections*, in *Objections to Christian Belief*, Constable, 1963 (pages 35-56).

be seen, quietly Christianised and modified for occidental use, in not a few of the authoritative, scientific, and even popular treatises of our present century.

The Perfumed Garden has been described as a panegyric of love, a song of sensual delights, a collection of joyous imaginings, a work of rare and curious erotic knowledge, a contribution to anthropological and ethnological research, useful alike to the student of languages, of Orientalism, and psychology. It is all of these, whatever the prudes may say. But those who have imagined it to be a mere work of imagination, devoted solely to the carnal excursions of arab lubricity, have fallen into the gravest of errors and misconceptions. Although the book deals quite frankly with numerous aspects of sex, it avoids the four-letter-word baldness and public-bar punctuation of many modern novels, and is completely devoid of any contrived obscenity. Throughout its pages one can, in fact, sense something of the natural Moslem reverence for that divine power resident in the cosmos; a power which, omnipotently and eternally, governs all things in heaven and on earth.

Highgate,
June, 1963.

SELECT BIBLIOGRAPHY

Most of my bibliographical references are contained in the footnotes to the Introduction. Some information comes from my private notes, made over many years of research. The following volumes, however, should prove especially useful for the reader who wishes to enlarge his picture:

MULK RAJ ANAND. *Kama Kala: Some Notes on the Philosophical Basis of Hindu Erotic Sculpture.* London, Charles Skilton, 1958 (illustrated).

(There are two companion volumes in the same series, invaluable for their subject matter, and interesting for purposes of comparison:

JEAN MARCADÉ. *Roma Amor: Essay on Erotic Elements in Etruscan and Roman Art.* London, Charles Skilton. 1961.

JEAN MARCADÉ. *Eros Kalos: Essay on Erotic Elements in Greek Art.* London, Charles Skilton, 1962.

LESLEY BLANCH. *The Wilder Shores of Love.* London, John Murray, 1954.

ISABEL BURTON. *The Life of Captain Sir Richard F. Burton, K.C.M.G., F.R.G.S.* (Two vols.). London, Chapman & Hall, 1893.

JEAN BURTON. *Sir Richard Burton's Wife.* London, Harrap, 1942.

SIR RICHARD F. BURTON. *A Plain and Literal Translation of the Arabian Nights' Entertainments, Now Entituled The Book of The Thousand Nights and a Night, With Introduction, Explanatory Notes . . . and a Terminal Essay* (Printed by the Kama Shastra Society For Private Subscribers Only). Sixteen volumes, 1885-8 (Numerous facsimile reprints of varying quality were printed in Denver, Colorado, usually in seventeen volumes – achieved by splitting the very large third 'Supplemental' volume into two, with continuous pagination as in the original. These reprints omit any reference to the Kama Shastra Society, and substitute: Printed by the Burton Club for private subscribers only).

FLORENT FELS. *L'Art et L'Amour.* Paris, Editions Arc-en-Ciel, 1952. (Two vols. quarto, with about 700 plates, some in colour). An English edition of this work, translated with revisions and some additional notes by Alan Hull Walton, is shortly to be published by Charles Skilton.

ALASTAIR HERON (ed.) *Towards a Quaker View of Sex.* London, Friends Home Service Committee, 1963.

LO DUCA. *A History of Eroticism.* Adapted from the French by Kenneth Anger. London, Rodney Books, 1963 (illustrated).

NORMAN M. PENZER. *An Annotated Bibliography of Sir Richard Francis Burton*, K.C.M.G. London, A. M. Philpot, 1923.

GEORGINA M. STISTED. *The True Life of Sir Richard F. Burton.* London, H. S. Nichols, 1896.

VATSYAYANA. *The Kama Sutra of Vatsyayana*, Translated by Sir Richard Burton and F. F. Arbuthnot. Edited with a Preface by W. G. Archer. Introduction by K. M. Panikkar. London, George Allen and Unwin, 1963.

THOMAS WRIGHT. *Life of Sir Richard Burton.* (Two vols.). London, 1906. (Wright and Lady Burton are not always reliable, and must be read with circumspection. See, on this point, Penzer's Bibliography).

*   *   *   *

There are two German editions of *The Perfumed Garden.* Details of the title-pages are included here for the assistance of those who might wish to make reference to them :

Der duftende Garten des Scheik Nefzaui. Ein arabische Ars amatoria. Deutsche Bearbeitung von H. Conrad. Privatdruck des Verlages 'Der Spiegel' zu Leipzig. (1905).

Liebe im Orient: Der duftende Garten des Scheik Nefzaui: erste vollständige deutsche Ausgabe, herausgegeben von Dr. F. Leiter und Dr. Hans H. Thal. Wien-Leipzig, 1929.

Recently three paper-back editions of Burton's translation of the *Kama Sutra* have appeared almost simultaneously. These are worth consultation for the new prefatory matter added in each case :

The Kama Sutra of Vatsyayana . . . Edited with foreword and notes by John Muirhead-Gould. Introduction by Dom Moraes. London, Panther Books, 1963.

John Muirhead-Gould's *Foreword* contains a valuable clarification of the bibliography of the Burton-Arbuthnot translation, pointing out the fact that textual differences exist in the original reprints of this translation. The short *Introduction* by Dom Moraes is also worthy of preservation.

The Kama Sutra of Vatsyayana and the Phaedrus of Plato . . . Edited with an Introduction by Kenneth Walker, M.A., F.R.C.S. London, Kimber Pocket Editions, 1963.

The translation of the *Phaedrus* given here is that of Benjamin Jowett, for long the standard and best-known of English versions. Kenneth Walker's *Introduction* is excellent, and stresses the folly of the Victorian attitude towards sex and sexual instruction.

Vatsyayana's Kama Sutra . . . With Introduction and Illustrations. London, Richard K. Champion, 1963.

This edition is well-printed on excellent quality paper. It contains an interesting unsigned new *Introduction*, inexplicably sandwiched between the *Original Preface* and the *Original Introduction*, and obviously written for the general reader.

A.H.W.

THE PERFUMED GARDEN

of the

CHEIKH NEFZAOUI

Translated by

SIR RICHARD BURTON

———————

NOTE TO THE 1886 EDITION

T H E *Perfumed Garden* was translated into French before the
year 1850, by a Staff Officer of the French army in Algeria.
An autograph edition, printed in the italic character, was
printed in 1876, but, as only twenty-five[1] copies are said to have
been made, the book is both rare and costly, while, from the
peculiarity of its type, it is difficult and fatiguing to read. An
admirable reprint has, however, been recently issued in Paris,
with the translator's notes and remarks, revised and corrected
by the light of the fuller knowledge of Algeria which has
been acquired since the translation was made.[2] From that last
edition the present translation (an exact and literal one) has
been made, and it is the first time that the work – one of the
most remarkable of its kind – has appeared in the English
language.

[1] The exact number of copies made is almost certainly 35.
(A.H.W.)
[2] The beautifully printed Liseux edition, issued at Paris,
1886, which might be described as the standard European
text. (A.H.W.)

NOTES OF THE TRANSLATOR
RESPECTING THE
CHEIKH NEFZAOUI[3]

THE NAME of the Cheikh has become known to posterity as the author of this work, which is the only one attributed to him.

In spite of the subject-matter of the book and the manifold errors found in it, and caused by the negligence and ignorance of the copyists, it is manifest that this treatise comes from the pen of a man of great erudition, who had a better knowledge in general of literature and medicine than is commonly found with Arabs.

According to the historical notice contained in the first leaves of the manuscript, and notwithstanding the apparent error respecting the name of the Bey who was reigning in Tunis, it may be presumed that this work was written in the beginning of the sixteenth century, about the year 925 of the Hegira.[4]

As regards the birthplace of the author, it may be taken for granted, considering that the Arabs habitually joined the name of their birthplace to their own, that he was born at Nefzaoua,[5]

[3] Note in the autograph edition, 1876: The reader will bear in mind in perusing this work that the remarks and notes by the eminent translator were written before 1850, when Algiers was but little known, and Kabylia in particular not at all. He will therefore not be surprised to find that some slight details are not on a level with the knowledge since acquired.

[4] As stated above, in a footnote to the Introduction (page 7), the date of the composition of the *Garden* may well have been earlier—i.e. between 1394 and 1433 A.D. (A.H.W.)

[5] The district of Nefzaoua contains many isolated villages, all on level ground, and surrounded by palm trees; with large reservoirs in their midst. The pilgrims believe that the land is called *Nefzaoua*, because there are in it a thousand *zaoua* (a chapel in which marabout is buried), and it is

a town situated in the district of that name on the shore of the lake Sebkha Melrir, in the south of the kingdom of Tunis.

The Cheikh himself records that he lived in Tunis, and it is most probable the book was written in that city. According to tradition, a particular motive induced him to undertake a work entirely at variance with his simple tastes and retired habits.

His knowledge of law and literature, as well as of medicine, having been reported to the Bey of Tunis, this ruler wished to invest him with the office of cadi, although he was unwilling to occupy himself with public functions.

As he, however, desired not to give the Bey cause for offence, whereby he might have incurred danger, he merely requested a short delay, in order to be able to finish a work which he had in hand.

This having been granted, he set himself to compose the treatise which was then occupying his mind, and which, becoming known, drew so much attention upon the author, that it became henceforth impossible to confide to him functions of the nature of those of a cadi.[6]

But this version, which is not supported by any authenticated proof, and which represents the Cheikh Nefzaoui as a man of light morals, does not seem to be admissible. One need only glance at the book to be convinced that its author was animated by the most praiseworthy intentions, and that, far from being in fault, he deserves gratitude for the services he has rendered to humanity. Contrary to the habits of the Arabs, there exists no commentary on this book; the reason may, perhaps be found in the nature of the subject of which it treats, and which may

alleged that the name was first El Afoun Zaouia, later corrupted into Nefzaoua. But this Arabian etymology does not appear to be correct, as according to the Arabian historians the names of the localities are older than the establishment of Islamism. The town of Nefzaoua is surrounded by a wall built of stones and bricks; having six gateways, one mosque, baths, and a market; in the environs are many wells and gardens.

[6] It is not impossible that the book, written in these circumstances, was only an abridgment of the present one, an abridgment which he refers to in the first chapter of this book under the name of *Torch of the Universe*.

have frightened, unnecessarily, the serious and the studious. I say unnecessarily, because this book, more than any other, ought to have commentaries; grave questions are treated in it, and open out a large field for work and meditation.

What can be more important, in fact, than the study of the principles upon which rest the happiness of man and woman, by reason of their mutual relations; relations which are themselves dependent upon character, health, temperament and the constitution, all of which it is the duty of philosophers to study.[7] I have endeavoured to rectify this omission by notes, which, incomplete as I know them to be, will still, to a certain point, serve for guidance.

In doubtful and difficult cases, and where the ideas of the author did not seem to be clearly set out, I have not hesitated to look for enlightenment to the savants of sundry confessions, and by their kind assistance many difficulties, which I believed insurmountable, were conquered. I am glad to render them here my thanks.

Amongst the authors who have treated of similar subjects, there is not one that can be entirely compared with the Cheikh; for his book reminds you, at the same time, of Aretin,[8] of the book *Conjugal Love*, and of Rabelais; the resemblance to this last is sometimes so striking that I could not resist the temptation to quote, in several places, analogous passages.

[7] 'We need not fear to compare the pleasures of the senses with the most intellectual pleasures; let us not fall into the delusion of believing that there are natural pleasures of two sorts, the one more ignoble than the other: the noblest pleasures are the greatest.' (*Essai de Philosophie Morale*, par M. de Maupertius, Berlin, 1749.)

[8] i.e. Aretino – *le divin Arétin*, also known as the 'Scourge of Princes' (*Flagello dei Principi*). This celebrated Italian poet and satirist was born at Arezzo, and lived between the years 1492 and 1557. The wit of his verses and plays brought him unusual popularity, but he is chiefly remembered for his *Sonnetti Lussuriosi* (16 sonnets descriptive of coital postures), and his *Ragionamenti* (or *Dialogues*) published between 1535 and 1538. See the important article by David Foxon in *The Book Collector*, Vol. 12, No. 2, Summer, 1963, pages 159-177 (illustrated), where he discusses 'Aretine's Postures', the *Ragionamenti*, and the *Puttana Errante* (which may not be by Aretino). (A.H.W.)

But what makes this treatise unique as a book of its kind, is the seriousness with which the most lascivious and obscene matters are presented. It is evident that the author is convinced of the importance of his subject, and that the desire to be of use to his fellow-men is the sole motive of his efforts.

With the view to give more weight to his recommendations, he does not hesitate to multiply his religious citations, and in many cases invokes even the authority of the Koran, the most sacred book of the Mussulmans.

It may be assumed that this book, without being exactly a compilation, is not entirely due to the genius of the Cheikh Nefzaoui, and that several parts may have been borrowed from Arabian and Indian writers. For instance, all the record of Moçailama and of Chedja is taken from the work of Mohammed ben Djerir el Taberi; the description of the different positions for coition, as well as the movements applicable to them, are borrowed from Indian works; finally, the book of *Birds and Flowers*, by Azeddine el Mocadecci, seems to have been consulted with respect to the interpretation of dreams. But an author certainly is to be commended for having surrounded himself with the lights of former savants, and it would be ingratitude not to acknowledge the benefit which his books have conferred upon people who were still in their infancy to the art of love.

It is only to be regretted that this work, so complete in many respects, is defective in so far as it makes no mention of a custom too common with the Arabs not to deserve particular attention. I speak of the taste so universal with the old Greeks and Romans, namely, the preference they give to a boy before a woman, or even to treat the latter as a boy.[9]

[9] Arabic manuscripts of the *Garden* do, of course, contain a section devoted to homosexuality, which is so common amongst the Arab peoples that it is accepted as natural. The translator, moreover, was perfectly aware of these facts, and his words here can only be taken as a deference to the predominant prejudice and ignorance of his period (see the Introduction to this volume, pages 19-20). Some interesting material relative to homosexuality amongst the Arabs today is to be found in : *Love in the East*, by George Allgrove, London, Anthony Gibbs & Phillips, 1962. See also the long section headed 'Pederasty' in the *Terminal Essay* to

There might have been given on this subject sound advice as well with regard to the pleasures mutually enjoyed by the women called *tribades*. The same reticence has been observed by the author with regard to *bestiality*. Nevertheless he does speak, in one story, (i.e. *The History of Zohra*, in the twenty-first and concluding chapter of the work), of the mutual caresses of two women; and he relates an anecdote concerning a woman who provoked the caresses of an ass (which, as explained in the Introduction, has been eliminated from the present edition), thus revealing that he knew of such matters.

Lastly, the Cheikh does not mention the pleasures which the mouth or the hand of a pretty woman can give, nor the *cunnilinges*.[10]

What may have been the motive for these omissions? The author's silence cannot be attributed to ignorance, for in the course of his work he has given proofs of an erudition too extended and various to permit a suspicion of his knowledge.

Burton's *Arabian Nights*, volume X, where he is far from reticent. Havelock Ellis, *Studies in the Psychology of Sex* (*Sexual Inversion*), pages 15, 22, 58 and 207 (Random House ed., New York, 1936, vol. 2, part 2) also supplies some references in this connection. The literature is vast. (A.H.W.)

[10] *Paediconibus os olere dicis;*
Hoc si, sicut ais, Fabulle, verum est,
Quid tu credis olere cunnilingis?
Martialis Book xii., Epig. 86.

—Pott and Wright's translation (London, Routledge, no date), and Bohn's edition (London, 1860; since reprinted by Bell & Sons), both print this epigram as epigram 85 of Book XII, and not as epigram 86. The order however, does vary in Latin texts, and it is not easy to say which Burton made reference to for purposes of checking. Graglia's Italian translation runs : *Tu di che la bocca sente cattivo ai sodomiti. Se questo, come tu dici, o Fabullo, e vero, che credi tu che senta ai cunnilingi?* Whilst *fellatio, cunnilinctus* (incorrectly called cunnilingus), and masturbation are certainly known to the Arab, as to the rest of the world, less given to the discussion of these matters than, for example, the ancient Roman writers and poets. Genito-oral contacts, etc., have been dealt with at length by Kinsey. (*Sexual behaviour in the Human Male*, but more especially in *Sexual Behaviour in the Human Female*), Havelock Ellis, and most of the authors of popular French, English, and American manuals of sexual instruction. The list is too lengthy for more than mere mention here. (A.H.W.)

Should we look for the cause of this gap to the contempt which the Mussulman in reality feels for woman, and owing to which he may think that it would be degrading to his dignity as a man to descend to caresses otherwise regulated than by the laws of nature? Or did the author perhaps, avoid the mention of similar matter out of fear that he might be suspected of sharing tastes which many people look upon as depraved?

However this may be, the book contains much useful information and a large number of curious cases, and I have undertaken the translation because, as the Cheikh Nefzaoui says in his preamble: 'I swear before God, certainly! the knowledge of this book is necessary. It will be only the shamefully ignorant, the enemy of all science, who does not read it, or who turns it into ridicule.'

THE PERFUMED GARDEN

INTRODUCTION

General Remarks About Coition

PRAISE BE GIVEN to God, who has placed man's greatest pleasure in the natural parts of woman, and has destined the natural parts of man to afford the greatest enjoyment to woman.[11]

He has not endowed the parts of woman with any pleasurable or satisfactory feeling until the same have been penetrated by the instrument of the male; and likewise the sexual organs of man know neither rest nor quietness until they have entered those of the female.

Hence the mutual operation. There takes place between the two actors wrestlings, intertwinings,[12] a kind of animated conflict.

[11] The Arabic manuscript used for the incompletely published Carrington English version of the *Garden* (see introduction, above, pages 23-4) was, of course, different from that used by the anonymous French Officer. The Carrington Manuscript seems to have been more complete in some respects, though the translation itself is marred by an undue and unjustifiable concentration on details (especially in the notes) which are absent from the much superior 'Autograph', Liseux, and Kama Shastra Society editions. The Carrington volume has its virtues, nevertheless; and for purposes of comparison, I reproduce below its opening passage:

'The Book Entitled The Perfumed Garden For The Soul's Delectation by the Shaykh Al-Imam Abu 'Abd-Allah An-Nafzawi – In the Name of Allah The Merciful, The Compassionate, May Prayer and Peace be upon our Lord and Master, Mohammed – The Learned Shaykh and Imam, The Great Scholar, The Worthy Exemplar and Most Intelligent, Abu 'Abd-Allah Mohammed Ibn 'Umar An-Nafzawi – May God Most High Have Pity upon Him, Amen! – Hath Said:

'Praise be given to God who hath lodged Man's greatest Pleasure in the Clefts of Women and caused the Joy of Women to centre in the Lance-points of Men. . . .' (*etc.*) (A.H.W.)

[12] The word *nitah*, used by the author, signifies the mutual attack of two horned animals, first knocking their heads together, and then stepping back, after having tried to interlace their horns; it is a quick interchange of blows between two combatants. The expression of the Arabic author is a simile which I could not easily reproduce.

Owing to the contact of the lower parts of the two bellies,[13] the enjoyment soon comes to pass. The man is at work as with a pestle, while the woman seconds him by lascivious movements;[14] finally comes the ejaculation.

The kiss on the mouth, on the two cheeks, upon the neck, as well as the sucking up of fresh lips, are gifts of God, destined to provoke erection at the favourable moment. God also was it who has embellished the chest of the woman with breasts, has furnished her with a double chin,[15] and has given brilliant colours to her cheeks.

He has also gifted her with eyes that inspire love, and with eyelashes like polished blades.

He has furnished her with a rounded belly and a beautiful navel, and with a majestic crupper; and all these wonders are borne up by the thighs. It is between these latter that God has placed the arena of the combat; when the same is provided with ample flesh, it resembles the head of a lion. It is called *vulva*. Oh! how many men's deaths lie at her door? Amongst them how many heroes!

God has furnished this object with a mouth, a tongue,[16] two

[13] The Arabic word *'Anah* designates the lower parts of the abdomen, usually hirsute, but does not, of itself signify the generative organs. (*original note corrected* by A.H.W.)

[14] In order to express the movement which takes place in the act of coition, the author uses the word *dok* with reference to the man, and *hez* for the woman. The first of these words means to concuss, to stamp, to pound; it is the action of the pestle in the mortar; the second word signifies a swinging movement, at once exciting, exhilarating, and lascivious.—It has been noted that the word *dok* (or *dakka*), carried precisely the same meaning as the vulgar English expression 'to have a grind'. Which is simply a vivid and very apt description of the movement of the male. As Burton said elsewhere, the Arab always calls a spade a spade. But this is the innocent expression of childhood, the humour of a people who have not been exposed to the corrupting influences of a decadent civilisation. It is *not* the facetious humour of sophistication. (A.H.W.)

[15] The word *gheba* means a double chin. The Arabs have a decided preference for fat women, consequently everything pointing to that condition is with them a beauty. Thus, the ridges forming upon the stomach of a woman by the development of their stoutness are a very seductive sight in the eyes of Arabs.

[16] Meaning the clitoris.

lips; it is like the impression of the hoof of the gazelle in the sands of the desert.

The whole is supported by two marvellous columns, testifying to the might and the wisdom of God; they are not too long nor too short; and they are graced with knees, calves, ankles, and heels, upon which rest precious rings.

Then the Almighty has plunged woman into a sea of splendours, of voluptuousness, and of delights, and covered her with precious vestments, with brilliant girdles and provoking smiles.

So let us praise and exalt him who has created woman and her beauties, with her appetising flesh; who has given her hairs, a beautiful figure, a bosom with breasts which are swelling, and amorous ways, which awaken desires.

The Master of the Universe has bestowed upon them the empire of seduction; all men, weak or strong, are subjected to the weakness for the love of woman. Through woman we have society or dispersion, sojourn or emigration.

The state of humility in which are the hearts of those who love and are separated from the object of their love, makes their hearts burn with love's fire; they are oppressed with a feeling of servitude, contempt and misery; they suffer under the vicissitudes of their passion: and all this as a consequence of their burning desire of contact.

I, the servant of God, am thankful to him that no one can help falling in love with beautiful women, and that no one can escape the desire to possess them, neither by change, nor flight, nor separation.

I testify that there is only one God, and that he has no associate. I shall adhere to this precious testimony to the day of the last judgment.

I likewise testify as to our lord and master, Mohammed, the servant and ambassador of God, the greatest of the prophets (the benediction and pity of God be with him and with his family and disciples!).[17] I keep prayers and benedictions for the day of retribution, that terrible moment.

The Origin of this Work

I HAVE written this magnificent work after a small book called *The Torch of the World*, which treats of the mysteries of generation.

This latter work came to the knowledge of the Vizir of our master Abd-el-Aziz, the ruler of Tunis.

This illustrious Vizir was his poet, his companion, his friend and private secretary. He was good in council, true, sagacious and wise, the best learned man of his time, and well acquainted with all things. He called himself Mohammed ben Ouana ez Zonaoui, and traced his origin from Zonaoua.[18] He had been brought up at Algiers, and in that town our master Abd-el-Aziz el Hafsi had made his acquaintance.[19]

---

[17] Mohammed, in verse 56, chap. xxxiii, with the heading 'The Confederates,' asks the believers to pray for him to God, and salute his name. It is in pursuance of this precept that the Mussulmans neither pronounce nor write the name of their prophet without adding the sacramental formula, which runs: 'Upon whom be benedictions and blessings of God.'

[18] The Zonaoua were an independent Kabyl tribe, occupying the high peaks of Djurjura. The land of Kon-Kon, represented by the Spanish writers as a kingdom, is simply the district belonging to the Zonaoua tribe, who had frequent conflicts with the Turks on their first arrival in Tunis.

[19] The period spoken of here can only be that of the submission of Algiers to Spain, when that city in 1510 (916 of the Hegira) acknowledged the supremacy of Spain and promised to pay her tribute, or that of the establishment of the Turkish domination in 1515 (921 of the Hegira). These are the only two cases of submission related by the old historians; and at neither of these periods was an Abd-el-Aziz reigning in Tunis. It is however very probable that the Author speaks of the Turkish occupation, when Barbarossa, having been invited by the Emir of Algiers to help him with his Turks in the war with the Spaniards, arrived at the city, put the Emir to death, and caused himself to be proclaimed King of Algiers instead.

The ruler of Tunis was then Abou Omar Amane Mohammed. The Bey of the name Abd-el-Aziz, who according to the period of his reign, came nearest to the events named by the author, was Abou Omar Abd-el-Aziz, who died in 893, and was one of the best Khelifar of the dynasty of the Beni Hafs. This error or difference will not surprise those who know how inaccurate the Arabs are in their quotations.

On the day when Algiers was taken, that ruler took flight with him to Tunis (which land may God preserve in his power till the day of resurrection), and named him his Grand Vizir.

When the above mentioned book came into his hands, he sent for me, and invited me pressingly to come and see him. I went forthwith to his house, and he received me most honorably. Three days after he came to me, and showing me my book, said, 'This is your work.' Seeing me blush, he added, 'You need not be ashamed; everything you have said in it is true; no one need be shocked at your words. Moreover, you are not the first who has treated of this matter; and I swear by God that it is necessary to know this book. It is only the shameless bore and the enemy of all science who will not read it, or make fun of it. But there are sundry things which you will have to treat about yet.' I asked him what these things were, and he answered, 'I wish that you would add to the work a supplement, treating of the remedies of which you have said nothing, and adding all the facts appertaining thereto, omitting nothing. You will describe in the same the motives of the act of generation, as well as the matters that prevent it. You will mention the means for undoing spells (aiguillette), and the way to increase the size of the virile member, when too small, and to make it resplendent. You will further cite those means which remove the unpleasant smells from the armpits and the natural parts of women, and those which will contract those parts. You will further speak of pregnancy, so as to make your book perfect and wanting in nothing. And, finally, you will have done your work, if your book satisfy all wishes.'

I replied to the Vizir: 'Oh, my master, all you have said here is not difficult to do, if it is the pleasure of God on high.'[20]

---

[20] The Arabs never say they will do a thing, without adding, 'If it please God.' The prescriptions of the Koran (verse 23, chap. xviii) run; 'Never say, I shall do so and so tomorrow,' without 'If it please God.'

The origin of this verse is ascribed to the momentary trouble in which Mohammed was, when answering questions put to him by Jews. He had promised to answer them the next day, forgetting to add, 'If it please

I forthwith went to work with the composition of this book, imploring the assistance of God (may he pour his blessing on his prophet, and may happiness and pity be with him).

I have called this work *The Perfumed Garden for the Soul's Recreation* (Er Roud el Âater p'nezaha el Khater).

And we pray to God, who directs everything for the best (and there is no other God than He, and there is nothing good that does not come from Him), to lend us His help, and lead us in good ways; for there is no power nor joy but in the high and mighty God.

I have divided this book into twenty-one chapters, in order to make it easier reading for the *taleb* (student) who wishes to learn, and to facilitate his search for what he wants. Each chapter relates to a particular subject, be it physical, or anecdotal, or treating of the wiles and deceits of women.

God.' As punishment the revelations did not come, till some days after. Their verse runs as follows :

'Never say, "I shall do a thing tomorrow," without adding "If it be the will of God." Remember God, if you should forget this, and say "Perhaps God will help me to the true knowledge of things".'

CHAPTER I

Concerning Praiseworthy Men

LEARN, O VIZIR (God's blessing be upon you), that there are different sorts of men and women; that amongst these are those who are worthy of praise, and those who deserve reproach.[21]

When a meritorious man finds himself near to women, his member grows, gets strong, vigorous and hard; he is not quick to discharge, and after the trembling caused by the emission of the sperm, he is soon stiff again.

Such a man is liked and appreciated by women; this is because the woman loves the man only for the sake of coition. His member should, therefore, be of ample dimensions and length. Such a man ought to be broad in the chest, and heavy in the crupper; he should know how to regulate his emission, and be ready as to erection; his member should reach to the end of the canal of the female, and completely fill the same in all its parts. Such an one will be well beloved by women, for, as the poet says:

> I have seen women trying to find in young men
> The durable qualities which grace the man of full power,
> The beauty, the enjoyment, the reserve, the strength,
> The full-formed member providing a lengthened coition,
> A heavy crupper, a slowly coming emission,

[21] Carrington reads thus: 'Know O Wazir! – May God have Compassion upon thee – that men and women are divided into different categories: to wit, those who are worthy of praise and those who draw upon themselves reproach.' (A.H.W.)

A lightsome chest, as it were floating upon them;
The spermal ejaculation slow to arrive, so as
To furnish forth a long drawn-out enjoyment.
His member soon to be prone again for erection,
To ply the plane²² again and again and again on their vulvas,
Such is the man whose cult gives pleasure to women,
And who will ever stand high in their esteem.

Qualities which Women are looking for in Men

The tale goes, that on a certain day, Abd-el-Melik ben Merouane,²³ went to see Leilla, his mistress,²⁴ and put various questions to her. Amongst other things, he asked her what were the qualities which women looked for in men.

Leilla answered him: 'Oh, my master, they must have cheeks like ours.' 'And what besides?' said Ben Merouane. She continued: 'And hairs like ours; finally they should be like to you, O prince of believers, for, surely, if a man is not strong and rich he will obtain nothing from women.'

Various Lengths of the Virile Member

The virile member, to please women, must have at most a length of the breadth of twelve fingers, or three hand-breadths, and at least six fingers, or a hand and a half breadth.

There are men with members of twelve fingers, or three hand-breadths; others of ten fingers, or two and a half hands. And

²² Note of the edition of 1876: The Arab word signifies, 'He flies, he works all around, he planes roundly through space.' This is a poetical image, difficult to render in translation.

²³ Abd-el-Melik ben Merouane was Kalif of Damascus; he reigned over Arabia, Syria, and part of the Orient. He lived about the year 76, for history reports that in that year he caused money to be coined with the legend. 'God is unique, God is alone.' His name is, besides, found on some coins older than the year 75.

²⁴ Leilla is a poetess, who lived at the time of the Kalif, Abd-el-Melik, the son of Merouane. She was also called *Akhegalia*, as belonging to an Arab family named '*the children of Akhegal*.' She is celebrated for the love she inspired Medjenoun with, and which was the subject of many romances.

others measure eight fingers, or two hands. A man whose member is of less dimensions cannot please women.[25]

The use of Perfumes in Coition. The History of Moçailama

The use of perfumes, by man as well as by woman, excites to the act of copulation. The woman, inhaling the perfumes employed by the man, becomes intoxicated; and the use of scents has often proved a strong help to man, and assisted him in getting possession of a woman.

On this subject it is told of Moçailama,[26] the impostor, the son of Kaiss (whom God may curse!), that he pretended to have the gift of prophecy, and imitated the Prophet of God (blessings and salutations to him). For which reasons he and a great number of Arabs have incurred the ire of the Almighty.

[25] It must be remembered that we are here dealing with the Arab race, in whom the genital dimensions are generally greater than in European man. The penile lengths would therefore be approximately as follows: Twelve finger-breadths represent 9 inches, which is rare in the Englishman, the Frenchman, and other Europeans. Ten finger-breadths are equivalent to $7\frac{1}{2}$ inches. Eight finger-breadths to 6 inches. And six finger-breadths indicate $4\frac{1}{2}$ inches. Kinsey, in a private letter to me, said that after making some thousands of measurements, he found that the average American male had a penile length of 6.3 inches in erection. A French medical man, measuring some hundreds of soldiers and sailors, found the average to be 14 to 15 cm. in length, in erection, by 35 to 38 mm. in diameter. He claimed that 'the average is exceeded, beginning at 4 cm. in diameter and 16 cm. in length.' Rockstro (*A Plain Talk on Sex Difficulties*, London, 1947), and H. M. and A. Stone (*A Marriage Manual*, London, 1936; and New York, same year), all place the European and American average at 6 inches, whilst Waldeyer and Van de Velde give the measurement at anything from 14 to 16 cm. (*Ideal Marriage*, London, 1928). Thus the average would seem to be $5\frac{1}{2}$ inches to $6\frac{1}{2}$ inches, with anything between 5 and 7 inches to be considered as normal. The Carrington version differs at the end of this paragraph by closing thus: 'But that man whose yard is superior to twelve finger-breadths or inferior to six of the same measure is of little good to women. . . .' Medical opinion, however, states that size is of much less importance in the marital act than tenderness in approach, emotional relatedness, and mastery in the technique of love-making. (A.H.W.)

[26] This Moçailama was one of the strongest competitors of Mohammed. He sprang from the tribe of Honcifa, in the province of Yamama. He was the head of a deputation sent by his tribe to the prophet Mohammed, and embraced Islamism in the year 9 of the Hegira.

Moçailama, the son of Kaiss, the impostor, misconstrued likewise the Koran by his lies and impostures; and on the subject of a
chapter of the Koran, which the angel Gabriel (Hail be to him) had
brought to the Prophet (the mercy of God and hail to him), people
of bad faith had gone to see Moçailama, who had told them, 'To
me also has the angel Gabriel[27] brought a similar chapter.'

He derided the chapter headed 'The Elephant,'[28] saying, 'In
this chapter of the Elephant I see the elephant. What is the
elephant? What does it mean? What is this quadruped? It has
a tail and a long trunk. Surely it is a creation of our God, the
magnificent.'

The chapter of the Koran named the *Kouter*[29] was also an
object of his controversy. He said, 'We have given you precious
stones for yourself, and in preference to any other man, but take
care not to be proud of them.'

Moçailama thus perverted sundry chapters in the Koran by
his lies and his impostures.

He had been at this work when he heard the Prophet (the
salutation and mercy of God be with him) spoken of. He heard
that after he had placed his venerable hands upon a bald head,
the hair had forthwith sprung up again; that when he spat into
a pit, the water came in abundantly, and that the dirty water
turned at once clean and good for drinking; that when he spat
into an eye that was blind or obscure, the sight was at once

[27] This angel plays a great part in the Koran, and consequently in other
Oriental books. He conveyed to Mohammed the heavenly revelations, and
forms part of that order of spirits which the Mussulmans call *Mokarrabine*,
which means approaching nearest to God.

[28] There is in fact a chapter of the Koran with the heading 'The Elephant.'
This chapter, the 105th, originated with a victory of the Prophet over an
Ethiopian prince; the white Elephant, on which the prince was mounted,
having knelt down as a sign of adoration at the sight of Mecca. Hence
the name of the chapter, which perpetuates the name of this victory. It was
this name that Moçailama tries to turn into ridicule, by pretending to see
only the name of an animal, and not to understand its real sense.

[29] The title of Chapter 108 of the Koran, *el Kouter*, signifies 'generosity,'
'liberality.' Moçailama pretended in his controversy that all the articles
which the first verse of the chapter declares to have been given to Mohammed had been previously placed at his disposition, so that he might reserve
for himself the best.

restored to it, and when he placed his hands upon the head of a child, saying, 'Live for a century,' the child lived to be a hundred years old.

When the disciples of Moçailama saw these things or heard speak of them, they came to him and said, 'Have you no knowledge of Mohammed and his doings?' He replied, 'I shall do better than that.'

Now, Moçailama was an enemy of God, and when he put his luckless hand on the head of someone who had not much hair, the man was at once quite bald; when he spat into a well with a scanty supply of water, sweet as it was, it was turned dirty by the will of God; if he spat into a suffering eye, that eye lost its sight at once, and when he laid his hand upon the head of an infant, saying, 'Live a hundred years,' the infant died within an hour.

Observe, my brethren, what happens to those whose eyes remain closed to the light, and who are deprived of the assistance of the Almighty!

And thus acted that woman of the Beni-Temim, called *Chedjâ el Temimia*, who pretended to be a prophetess. She had heard of Moçailama, and he likewise of her.

This woman was powerful, for the Beni-Temim form a numerous tribe. She said, 'Prophecy cannot belong to two persons. Either he is a prophet, and then I and my disciples will follow his laws, or I am a prophetess, and then he and his disciples will follow my laws.'

This happened after the death of the Prophet (the salutation and mercy of God be with him).

Chedjâ then wrote to Moçailama a letter, in which she told him, 'It is not proper that two persons should at one and the same time profess prophecy; it is for one only to be a prophet. We will meet, we and our disciples, and examine each other. We shall discuss about that which has come to us from God (the Koran), and we will follow the laws of him who shall be acknowledged as the true prophet.'

F

She then closed her letter and gave it to a messenger, saying to him: 'Betake yourself, with this missive, to Yamama, and give it to Moçailama ben Kaiss. As for myself, I follow you, with the army.'

Next day the prophetess mounted horse, with her *goum*,[30] and followed the spoor of her envoy. When the latter arrived at Moçailama's place, he greeted him and gave him the letter.

Moçailama opened and read it, and understood its contents. He was dismayed, and began to advise with the people of his *goum*, one after another, but he did not see anything in their advice or in their views that could rid him of his embarrassment.

While he was in this perplexity, one of the superior men of his *goum* came forward and said to him: 'Oh, Moçailama, calm your soul and cool your eye.[31] I will give you the advice of a father to his son.'

Moçailama said to him: 'Speak, and may thy words be true.'

And the other one said: 'Tomorrow morning erect outside the city a tent of coloured brocades, provided with silk furniture of all sorts.[32] Fill the tent afterwards with a variety of different perfumes, amber, musk, and all sorts of scents, as rose, orange flowers, jonquils, jessamine, hyacinth, carnation and other plants. This done, have then placed there several gold censers filled with green aloes, ambergris, *nedde*[33] and so on. Then fix the hangings so that nothing of these perfumes can escape out of the tent. Then, when you find the vapour strong enough to

[30] *Goum*: meeting of cavaliers, who form an escort, sometimes representing the war-forces of great Arab chiefs. Perhaps in the sense used by the author the word may be rendered as disciples.

[31] One hears frequently, 'May God refresh his eyes,' which means: 'May God by contentment refresh his eye, which is hot with tears.'

[32] It will, perhaps, not be useless to observe here that among the nomadical Arabs the custom obtains that the man who wants to cohabit with his wife erects a tent over her. Hence a man who is going to be married is called *bani*, building; and of a man who has just been married it is said, '*Bena ala Ahlihi*,' which means: 'He has built over his wife.'

[33] The *nedde* is a mixture of various perfumes, amongst which benzoin and amber predominate. This mixture, which is black, is formed into a small cylinder. It is burnt upon coals, or like the pastils of the serail by lighting one end. According to some authors, *nedde* is only a preparation of amber.

impregnate water,[34] sit down on your throne, and send for the prophetess to come and see you in the tent, where she will be alone with you. When you are thus together there, and she inhales the perfumes, she will delight in the same, all her bones will be relaxed in a soft repose, and finally she will be swooning. When you see her thus far gone, ask her to grant you her favours; she will not hesitate to accord them. Having once possessed her, you will be freed of the embarrassment caused to you by her and her *goum*.'

Moçailama exclaimed: 'You have spoken well. As God lives, your advice is good and well thought out.' And he had everything arranged accordingly.

When he saw that the perfumed vapour was dense enough to impregnate the water in the tent he sat down upon his throne and sent for the prophetess. On her arrival he gave orders to admit her into the tent; she entered and remained alone with him. He engaged her in conversation.

While Moçailama spoke to her she lost all her presence of mind, and became embarrassed and confused.

When he saw her in that state he knew that she desired cohabitation, and he said: 'Come, rise and let me have possession of you; this place has been prepared for that purpose. If you like you may lie on your back, or you can place yourself on all fours, or kneel as in prayer, with your brow touching the ground, and your crupper in the air, forming a tripod.[35]

[34] That is to say that the vapours of the perfumes have been long enough in the place and thick enough to communicate their odour to water placed in the tent. The text says only 'when the water shall be mixed with the fumes.'

[35] To understand this passage properly it must be known that the Arabs, when praying, kneel on the ground with the face bent low down and the hands on the knees.

The tripod is then formed by the two knees and the head touching the ground. It is easy to see that this position causes the posterior part of the body to project very much backwards. The method of performing cohabitation thus is stated in the 6th manner, chapter vi. '*Hoc mihi tradidit Deus: foeminas Deus condidit rimosas, virosque iis dedit maritos, qui mentulas in ipsas immittunt; eas que deinde simul ac volunt retrahunt: quo facto illae catulos nobis pariunt.*'

Whichever position you prefer, speak, and you shall be satisfied.'

The prophetess answered, 'I want it done in all ways. Let the revelation of God descend upon me, O Prophet of the Almighty.'

He at once precipitated himself upon her, and enjoyed her as he liked. She then said to him, 'When I am gone from here, ask my *goum* to give me to you in marriage.'

When she had left the tent and met her disciples, they said to her, 'What is the result of the conference, O prophetess of God?' and she replied, 'Moçailama has shown me what has been revealed to him, and I found it to be the truth, so obey him.'

Then Moçailama asked her in marriage from the *goum*, which was accorded to him. When the *goum* asked about the marriage-dowry of his future wife, he told them, 'I dispense you from saying the prayer *"aceur"'* (which is said at three or four o' clock). Ever from that time the Beni-Temim do not pray at that hour; and when they are asked the reason, they answer, 'It is on account of our prophetess; she only knows the way to the truth.' And, in fact, they recognized no other prophet.

On this subject a poet has said:

> For us a female prophet has arisen;
> Her laws we follow; for the rest of mankind
> The prophets that appeared were always men.[36]

The death of Moçailama was foretold by the prophecy of Abou Beker[37] (to whom God be good). He was, in fact, killed by Zeid ben Khettab. Other people say it was done by Ouhcha, one of his disciples. God only knows whether it was Ouhcha. He him-

[36] This history of the encounter between Moçailama and Chedja, whose proper name was Fedjah bent el Harents ben Souard, is reproduced in the work of Abou Djaferi Mohammed ben Djerir el Teberi, where it is told with the minutest particulars, and bears the signs of a veritable religious truth.

[37] Abou Beker is the father of Aïcha, the wife of Mohammed. He followed the latter in the year 11 of the Hegira. By his and Omar's authority, a great many Mussulmans were turned from their design to apostasize. He was the first Kalif, and remained in power, in spite of the pretensions of the partisans of Ali Mohammed's son-in-law, who maintained that the Prophet had long before his death assigned Ali as his successor.

self says on this point, 'I have killed in my ignorance the best of men, Haman ben Abd el Mosaleb,[38] and then I killed the worst of men, Moçailama. I hope that God will pardon one of these actions in consideration of the other.'

The meaning of these words, 'I have killed the best of men' is, that Ouhcha, before having yet known the prophet, had killed Hamza (to whom God be good), and having afterwards embraced Islamism, he killed Moçailama.

As regards Chedja et Temimia, she repented by God's grace, and took to the Islamitic faith; she married one of the Prophet's followers (God be good to her husband).

Thus finishes the story.

The man who deserves favours is, in the eyes of women, the one who is anxious to please them. He must be of good presence, excel in beauty those around him, be of good shape and well-formed proportions; true and sincere in his speech with women; he must likewise be generous and brave, not vainglorious, and pleasant in conversation. A slave to his promise, he must always keep his word, ever speak the truth, and do what he has said.

The man who boasts of his relations with women, of their acquaintance and good will to him, is a dastard. He will be spoken of in the next chapter.

There is a story that once there lived a king named Mamoum,[39] who had a court fool of the name of Bahloul,[40] who amused the princes and Vizirs.

One day this buffoon appeared before the King, who was

[38] These facts concur with the historical ones. Hamza, the uncle of the Prophet, was certainly killed in the battle of Ohod, in the year 4 of the Hegira, by a negro, Ouhcha, who afterwards killed Moçailama.

[39] Abdallah ben Mamoum, one of the sons of Haroun er Rachid. Having for a long time made war upon his brother el Amine for the empire, and the latter having been vanquished and killed in a battle near Bagdad, el Mamoum was unanimously proclaimed as Kalif in the year 178 of the Hegira. He was one of the most distinguished Abyssidian rulers with respect to science, wisdom, and goodness.

[40] The word Bahloul, of Persian origin, signifies a man that laughs, derides, a knave, a sort of fool in the Orient.

amusing himself. The King bade him to sit down, and then asked
him, turning away, 'Why hast thou come, O son of a bad
woman?'

Bahloul answered, 'I have come to see what has come to our
Lord, whom may God make victorious.'

'And what has come to thee?' replied the King, 'and how art
thou getting on with thy new and with thy old wife?' For
Bahloul, not content with one wife, had married a second one.

'I am not happy,' he answered, 'neither with the old one, nor
with the new one; and moreover poverty over-powers me.'

The King said, 'Can you recite any verses on this subject?'

The buffoon having answered in the affirmative, Mamoum
commanded him to recite those he knew, and Bahloul began as
follows:

> Poverty holds me in chains; misery torments me:
> I am being scourged with all misfortunes;
> Ill luck has cast me in trouble and peril,
> And has drawn upon me the contempt of man.
> God does not favour a poverty like mine;
> That is opprobrius in every one's eyes.
> Misfortune and misery for a long time
> Have held me tightly; and no doubt of it
> My dwelling house will soon not know me more.

Mamoum said to him, 'Where are you going to?'

He replied, 'To God and his Prophet, O prince of the believers.'

'That is well!' said the King; 'those who take refuge in God
and his Prophet, and then in us, will be made welcome. But can
you now tell me some more verses about your two wives, and
about what comes to pass with them?'

'Certainly,' said Bahloul.

'Then let us hear what you have to say!'

Bahloul then began thus with poetical words:

> By reason of my ignorance I have married two wives –
> And why do you complain, O husband of two wives?
> I said to myself, I shall be like a lamb between them;
> I shall take my pleasure upon the bosoms of my two sheep,
> And I have become like a ram between two female jackals,
> Days follow upon days, and nights upon nights,

And their yoke bears me down during both days and nights.
If I am kind to one, the other gets vexed.
And so I cannot escape from these two furies.
If you want to live well and with a free heart,
And with your hands unclenched, then do not marry.
If you must wed, then marry one wife only:
One alone is enough to satisfy two armies.

When Mamoum heard these words he began to laugh, till he nearly tumbled over. Then, as a proof of his kindness, he gave to Bahloul his golden robe, a most beautiful vestment.

Bahloul went in high spirits towards the dwelling of the Grand Vizir. Just then Hamdonna[41] looked from the height of her palace in that direction, and saw him. She said to her negress, 'By the God of the temple of Mecca! There is Bahloul dressed in a fine gold-worked robe! How can I manage to get possession of the same?'

The negress said, 'Oh, my mistress, you would not know how to get hold of that robe.'

Hamdonna answered, 'I have thought of a trick whereby to achieve my ends, and I shall get the robe from him.'

'Bahloul is a sly man,' replied the negress. 'People think generally that they can make fun of him; but, for God, it is he who makes fun of them. Give up the idea, mistress mine, and take care that you do not fall into the snare which you intend setting for him.'

But Hamdonna said again, 'It must be done!' She then sent her negress to Bahloul, to tell him that he should come to her.

He said, 'By the blessing of God, to him who calls you, you shall make answer,' and went to Hamdonna.[42]

Hamdonna welcomed him and said: 'Oh, Bahloul, I believe

---

[41] *Hamdonna* from the Arabic root *hamd*, which means to praise; hence *Ahmed*, the most praiseworthy. From the same root comes the name of *Mohammed* corrupted into *Mahomet*.

[42] 'To him who calls you make answer.' This sentence is taken from the *Hadits*, or Traditions of Mohammed. Sometimes it is used in conversation in the same sense as above, but its true meaning is obscure. The words 'By the blessing of God, in the same sentence, is a form of acceptance or consent.

you come to hear me sing.' He replied: 'Most certainly, oh, my mistress! You have a marvellous gift for singing.'

'I also think that after having listened to my songs, you will be pleased to take some refreshments.'

'Yes,' said he.

Then she began to sing admirably, so as to make people who listened die with love.

After Bahloul had heard her sing, refreshments were served; he ate, and he drank. Then she said to him: 'I do not know why, but I fancy you would gladly take off your robe, to make me a present of it.' And Bahloul answered: 'Oh, my mistress! I have sworn to give it to her to whom I have done as a man does to a woman.'

'Do you know what that is, Bahloul?' said she.

'Do I know it?' replied he. 'I, who am instructing God's creatures in that science? It is I who make them copulate in love, who initiate them in the delights a female can give, show them how one must caress a woman, and what will excite and satisfy her. Oh, my mistress, who should know the art of coition if it is not I?'

Hamdonna was the daughter of Mamoum, and the wife of the Grand Vizir. She was endowed with the most perfect beauty; of a superb figure and harmonious form. No one in her time surpassed her in grace and perfection. Heroes on seeing her became humble and submissive, and looked down to the ground for fear of temptation, so many charms and perfections had God lavished on her. Those who looked steadily at her were troubled in their mind, and oh! how many heroes imperilled themselves for her sake. For this very reason Bahloul had always avoided meeting her for fear of succumbing to the temptation; and, apprehensive for his peace of mind, had never, until then, been in her presence.

Bahloul began to converse with her. Now he looked at her and anon bent his eyes to the ground, fearful of not being able to command his passion. Hamdonna burnt with desire to have the robe, and he would not give it up without being paid for it.

'What price do you demand,' she asked. To which he replied, 'Coition, O apple of my eye.'

'You know what that is, O Bahloul?' said she.

'By God,' he cried; 'no man knows women better than I; they are the occupation of my life. No one has studied all their concerns more than I. I know what they are fond of; for learn, oh, lady mine, that men choose different occupations according to their genius and their bent.[43] The one takes, the other gives; this one sells, the other buys. My only thought is of love and of the possession of beautiful women. I heal those that are lovesick, and carry a solace to their thirsting vaginas.'

Hamdonna was surprised at his words and the sweetness of his language. 'Could you recite me some verses on this subject?' she asked.

'Certainly,' he answered.

'Very well, O Bahloul, let me hear what you have to say.' Bahloul recited as follows:

> Men are divided according to their affairs and doings;
> Some are always in spirits and joyful, others in tears.
> There are those whose life is restless and full of misery,
> While, on the contrary, others are steeped in good fortune,
> Always in luck's happy way, and favoured in all things.
> I alone am indifferent to all such matters.
> What care I for Turkomans, Persians, and Arabs?
> My whole ambition is in love and coition with women,
> No doubt nor mistake about that!
> If my member is without vulva, my state becomes frightful,
> My heart then burns with a fire which cannot be quenched.
> Look at my member erect! There it is – admire its beauty!
> It calms the heat of love and quenches the hottest fires
> By its movement in and out between your thighs.
> Oh, my hope and my apple, oh, noble and generous lady,

[43] In the original Arabic this is one of the passages in *Saja*, or rhymed prose. Burton has rendered many such passages in his translation of the *Arabian Nights*. The Carrington edition of the *Garden*, copying Burton's method, renders the above passage thus:

'No soul that breatheth can vie with me in the knowledge of women and how to deal and behave with them. Their true worth I know; their sicknesses to righten am I not slow; their flames can I put out howe'er they blow; their secrets keep in weal and woe . . .' (*etc.*) (A.H.W.)

If one time will not suffice to appease thy fire,
I shall do it again, so as to give satisfaction;
No one may reproach thee, for all the world does the same.
But if you choose to deny me, then send me away!
Chase me away from thy presence without any fear or remorse!
Yet bethink thee, and speak and augment not my trouble,
But, in the name of God, forgive me and do not reproach me.
While I am here let thy words be kind and forgiving.
Let them not fall upon me like sword-blades, keen and cutting!
Let me come to you and do not repel me.
Let me come to you like one that brings drink to the thirsty;
Hasten and let my hungry eyes look at thy bosom.
Do not withhold from me love's joys, and do not be bashful,
Give yourself up to me – I shall never cause you trouble,
Even were you to fill me with sickness from head to foot.
I shall always remain as I am, and you as you are,
Knowing that I am the servant, and you are the mistress ever.
Then shall our love be veiled? It shall be hidden for all time,
For I keep it a secret and I shall be mute and muzzled.
It is by God's will that everything happens,
And he has filled me with love; but today my luck is ill.

While Hamdonna was listening she nearly swooned, and set herself to examine the member of Bahloul, which stood erect like a column between his thighs. Now she said to herself: 'I shall give myself up to him,' and now, 'No I will not.' During this uncertainty she felt a yearning for pleasure deep within her parts privy; and Eblis made flow from her natural parts a moisture, the fore-runner of pleasure.[44] She then no longer combated her desire to cohabit with him, and reassured herself by the thought: 'If this Bahloul, after having had his pleasure with me, should divulge it no one will believe his words.'

She requested him to divest himself of his robe and to come into her room, but Bahloul replied: 'I shall not undress till I have sated my desire, O apple of my eye.'

Then Hamdonna rose, trembling with excitement for what was to follow; she undid her girdle, and left the room, Bahloul

[44] The words 'Eblis made flow a moisture' (*djéra Eblis menha medjéra el dem*) is an Arabian idiom, expressing the fact that a woman is getting lusty; the sexual parts grow moist. Eblis is a rebellious angel who refused to bow down before Adam when God ordered him to do so. Sometimes Eblis is also used as a general name for the devil, Satan, demon.

following her and thinking: 'Am I really awake or is this a dream?' He walked after her till she had entered her boudoir. Then she threw herself on a couch of silk, which was rounded on the top like a vault, lifted her clothes up over her thighs, trembling all over, and all the beauty which God had given her was in Bahloul's arms.

Bahloul examined the belly of Hamdonna, round like an elegant cupola, his eyes dwelt upon a navel which was like a pearl in a golden cup; and descending lower down there was a beautiful piece of nature's workmanship, and the whiteness and shape of her thighs surprised him.

Then he pressed Hamdonna in a passionate embrace, and soon saw the animation leave her face; she seemed almost unconscious. She had lost her head; and holding Bahloul's member in her hands, excited and fired him more and more.

Bahloul said to her: 'Why do I see you so troubled and beside yourself?' And she answered: 'Leave me, O son of a debauched woman! By God, I am like a mare in heat, and you continue to excite me still more with your words, and what words! They would set any woman on fire, if she was the purest creature in the world. You will insist in making me succumb by your talk and your verses.'

Bahloul answered: 'Am I then not like your husband?' 'Yes,' she said, 'but a woman gets heat on account of the man, as a mare on acount of the horse, whether the man be the husband or not; with this difference, however, that the mare gets lusty only at certain periods of the year, and only then receives the stallion, while a woman can always be made rampant by words of love.[45] Both these dispositions have met within me, and, as my husband is absent, make haste, for he will soon be back.'

[45] Rabelais says on the subject of women who, against the laws of nature go on receiving the embraces of men after having conceived: 'And if anybody should blame them for allowing men to explore them when full, considering that beasts in the like case never endure the male to enter, they will say that those are beasts: but they are women, making use of their right of superfetation.'

Bahloul replied: 'Oh, my mistress, my loins hurt me and prevent me mounting upon you. You take the man's position, and then take my robe and let me depart.'

Then he laid himself down in the position the woman takes in receiving a man; and his verge was standing up like a column.

Hamdonna threw herself upon Bahloul, took his member between her hands and began to look at it. She was astonished at its size, strength and firmness, and cried: 'Here we have the ruin of all women and the cause of many troubles. O Bahloul! I never saw a more beautiful dart than yours!' Still she continued keeping hold of it, and rubbed its head against the lips of her vulva till the latter part seemed to say: 'O member, come into me.'

Then Bahloul inserted his member into the vagina of the Sultan's daughter, and she, settling down upon his engine, allowed it to penetrate entirely into her furnace till nothing more could be seen of it, not the slightest trace, and she said: 'How lascivious has God made woman, and how indefatigable after her pleasures.' She then gave herself up to an up-and-down dance, moving her bottom like a riddle; to the right and left, and forward and backward; never was there such a dance as this.

The Sultan's daughter continued her ride upon Bahloul's member till the moment of enjoyment arrived, and the attraction[46] of the vulva seemed to pump the member as though by suction: just as an infant sucks the teat of the mother. The acme of enjoyment came to both simultaneously, and each took the pleasure with avidity.

Then Hamdonna seized the member in order to with-draw it, and slowly, slowly she made it come out, saying: 'This is the deed of a vigorous man.' Then she dried it and her own private parts with a silken kerchief, and rose.

Bahloul also got up and prepared to depart, but she said, 'And the robe?'

[46] The word *djadeba* (attraction) comes from an Arab root, *djedeb*, which means 'attract, drain, pump.' It appears several times in this work, and I believe it corresponds with a peculiarity found in some favoured women called 'nut-cracker.'

He answered, 'Why, O mistress! You have been riding me, and still want a present?'

'But,' said she, 'did you not tell me that you could not mount me on account of the pains in your loins?'

'It matters but little,' said Bahloul. 'The first time it was your turn, the second will be mine, and the price for it will be the robe, and then I will go.'

Hamdonna thought to herself, 'As he began he may now go on; afterwards he will go away.'

So she laid herself down, but Bahloul said, 'I shall not lie with you unless you undress entirely.'

Then she undressed until she was quite naked, and Bahloul fell into an ecstasy on seeing the beauty and perfection of her form. He looked at her magnificent thighs and rebounding navel, at her belly vaulted like an arch, her plump breasts standing out like hyacinths. Her neck was like a gazelle's, the opening of her mouth like a ring, her lips fresh and red like a gory sabre. Her teeth might have been taken for pearls and her cheeks for roses. Her eyes were black and well slit, and her eyebrows of ebony resembled the rounded flourish of the noun[47] traced by the hand of a skilful writer. Her forehead was like the full moon in the night.

Bahloul began to embrace her, to suck her lips and to kiss her bosom; he drew her fresh saliva and bit her thighs. So he went on till she was ready to swoon, and could scarcely stammer, and her eyes became veiled. Then he kissed her vulva, and she moved neither hand nor foot. He looked lovingly upon the secret parts of Hamdonna, beautiful enough to attract all eyes with their purple centre.[48]

Bahloul cried, 'Oh, the temptation of man!' and still he bit

[47] Noun is a letter of the Arabian alphabet, corresponding to our 'N'. Its half-circular form explains the comparison made by the author with reference to arched eyebrows.

[48] The word, which really means 'biting,' is used for all sorts of caresses in which the lips, the teeth, and even the tongue take part. It is, therefore, wrong to conclude from this passage that Bahloul indulged in the exercise of cunnilinge.

her and kissed her till her desire was roused to its full pitch. Her sighs came quicker, and grasping his member with her hand she made it disappear in her vagina.

Then it was he who moved hard, and she who responded hotly, the overwhelming pleasure simultaneously calming their fervour.

Then Bahloul got off her, dried his pestle and her mortar, and prepared to retire. But Hamdonna said, 'Where is the robe? You mock me, O Bahloul.' He answered, 'O my mistress, I shall only part with it for a consideration. You have had your dues and I mine. The first time was for you, the second time for me; now the third time shall be for the robe.'

This said, he took it off, folded it, and put it in Hamdonna's hands, who, having risen, laid down again on the couch and said, 'Do what you like!'

Forthwith Bahloul threw himself upon her, and with one push completely buried his member in her vagina; then he began to work as with a pestle, and she to move her bottom, until both again did flow over at the same time. Then he rose from her side, left his robe, and went.

The negress said to Hamdonna, 'O my mistress, is it not as I have told you? Bahloul is a bad man, and you could not get the better of him. They consider him as a subject for mockery, but, before God, he is making fun of them. Why would you not believe me?'

Hamdonna turned to her and said, 'Do not tire me with your remarks. It came to pass what had to come to pass, and on the opening of each vulva is inscribed the name of the man who is to enter[49] it, right or wrong, for love or for hatred. If Bahloul's name had not been inscribed on my vulva he would never have got into it, had he offered me the universe with all it contains.'

As they were thus talking there came a knock at the door.

[49] These words, 'each vulva, etc.' (*Koul ferdj mektoub ali esm nakahon*) allude to the phrase taken from the traditions left by Mohammed and often repeated by Mussulmans, 'Each man has his destiny written on his forehead, and no one can take it off.'

The negress asked who was there, and in answer the voice of Bahloul said, 'It is I.' Hamdonna, in doubt as to what the buffoon wanted to do, got frightened. The negress asked Bahloul what he wanted, and received the reply, 'Bring me a little water.' She went out of the house with a cup full of water. Bahloul drank, and then let the cup slip out of his hands, and it was broken. The negress shut the door upon Bahloul, who sat himself down on the threshold.

The buffoon being thus close to the door, the Vizir, Hamdonna's husband, arrived, who said to him, 'Why do I see you here, O Bahloul?' And he answered, 'O my lord, I was passing through this street when I was overcome by a great thirst. A negress came and brought me a cup of water. The cup slipped from my hands and got broken. Then our lady Hamdonna took my robe, which the Sultan our Master had given me as indemnification.'

Then said the Vizir, 'Let him have his robe.' Hamdonna at this moment came out, and her husband asked her whether it was true that she had taken the robe in payment for the cup. Hamdonna then cried, beating her hands together, 'What have you done, O Bahloul?' He answered, 'I have talked to your husband the language of my folly; talk to him, you, the language of thy wisdom.' And she, enraptured with the cunning he had displayed, gave him back his robe, and he departed.

CHAPTER II

Concerning Women who Deserve to be Praised

K NOW, O VIZIR (and the mercy of God be with you!) that there are women of all sorts; that there are such as are worthy of praise, and such as deserve nothing but contempt.

In order that a woman may be relished by men, she must have a perfect waist, and must be plump and lusty. Her hair will be black, her forehead wide, she will have eyebrows of Ethiopian blackness, large black eyes, with the whites in them very limpid. With cheek of perfect oval, she will have an elegant nose and a graceful mouth; lips and tongue vermilion; her breath will be of pleasant odour, her throat long, her neck strong, her bust and her belly large; her breasts must be full and firm, her belly in good proportion, and her navel well-developed and marked; the lower part of the belly is to be large, the vulva projecting and fleshy, from the point where the hairs grow, to the buttocks; the conduit must be narrow and not moist, soft to the touch, and emitting a strong heat and no bad smell; she must have the thighs and buttocks hard, the hips large and full, a waist of fine shape, hands and feet of striking elegance, plump arms, and well-developed shoulders.

If one looks at a woman with those qualities in front, one is fascinated; if from behind, one dies with pleasure. Looked at sitting, she is a rounded dome; lying, a soft-bed; standing, the staff of a standard. When she is walking, her natural parts appear as set off under her clothing. She speaks and laughs rarely, and never without a reason. She never leaves the house, even to see neighbours of her acquaintance. She has no women friends, gives her confidence to nobody, and her husband is her sole reliance. She takes nothing from anyone, excepting from her husband and her parents. If she sees relatives, she does not meddle with their affairs. She is not treacherous, and has no faults to hide, nor bad reasons to proffer. She does not try to entice people. If her husband shows his intention of performing the conjugal rite, she is agreeable to his desires and occasionally even provokes them. She assists him always in his affairs, and is sparing in complaints and tears; she does not laugh or rejoice when she sees her husband moody or sorrowful, but shares his troubles, and wheedles him into good humour, till he is quite content again. She does not surrender herself to anybody but her husband, even if abstinence would kill her. She hides her secret parts, and does not allow them to be seen; she is always elegantly attired, of the utmost personal propriety, and takes care not to let her husband see what might be repugnant to him. She perfumes herself with scents, uses antimony for her toilets, and cleans her teeth with *souak*.[50]

Such a woman is cherished by all men.

The Story of the Negro Dorérame[51]

The story goes, and God knows its truth, that there was once a powerful King who had a large kingdom, armies and allies. His name was Ali ben Direme.

One night, not being able to sleep at all, he called his Vizir, the Chief of the Police, and the Commander of his Guards. They presented themselves before him without delay, and he ordered

---

[50] *Souak* is the bark of the walnut tree, which has the quality to clean the teeth and redden the lips and gums. *Souak* means also toothpicks.
[51] This name is derived from an Arab word, which means to be ferocious, hard, etc.

G

them to arm themselves with their swords. They did so at once, and asked him, 'What news is there?'

He told them: 'Sleep will not come to me; I wish to walk through the town tonight, and I must have you ready at my hand during my round.'

'To hear is to obey,' they replied.

The King then left, saying: 'In the name of God! and may the blessing of the Prophet be with us, and benediction and mercy be with him.'

His suite followed, and accompanied him everywhere from street to street.

So they went on, until they heard a noise in one of the streets, and saw a man in the most violent passion stretched on the ground, face downwards, beating his breast with a stone and crying, 'Ah there is no longer any justice here below! Is there nobody who will tell the King what is going on in his states?' And he repeated incessantly: 'There is no longer any justice! she has disappeared and the whole world is in mourning.'

The King said to his attendants, 'Bring this man to me quietly, and be careful not to frighten him.' They went to him, took him by the hand, and said to him, 'Rise and have no fear – no harm will come to you.'

To which the man made answer, 'You tell me that I shall not come to harm, and have nothing to be afraid of, and still you do not bid me welcome! And you know that the welcome of a believer is a warrant of security and forgiveness.[52] Then, if the believer does not welcome the believer there is certainly ground for fear.' He then got up, and went with them towards the King.

The King stood still, hiding his face with his *kaïk*, as also did his attendants. The latter had their swords in their hands, and leant upon them.

When the man had come close to the King, he said, 'Greetings

[52] The author plays with the word *selam*, which has two meanings – Security, the state of a man who is right and safe; and greeting, welcome. *Es Selam alik* is the formula employed as welcome.

be with you, O man!' The King answered, 'I return your greetings, O man!' Then the man, 'Why say you "O man?"' The King, 'And why did you say "O man?"' 'It is because I do not know your name.' 'And likewise I do not know yours!'

The King then asked him, 'What mean these words I have heard: "Ah! there is no more justice here below! Nobody tells the King what is going on in his states!" Tell me what has happened to you.' 'I shall tell it only to that man who can avenge me and free me from oppression and shame, if it so please Almighty God!'

The King said to him, 'May God place me at your disposal for your revenge and deliverance from oppression and shame?'

'What I shall now tell you,' said the man, 'is marvellous and surprising. I loved a woman, who loved me also, and we were united in love. These relations lasted a long while, until an old woman enticed my mistress and took her away to a house of misfortune, shame and debauchery. Then sleep fled from my couch; I have lost all my happiness, and I have fallen into the abyss of misfortune.'

The King then said to him, 'Which is that house of ill omen, and with whom is the woman?'

The man replied, 'She is with a negro of the name of Dorérame, who has at his house women beautiful as the moon, the likes of whom the King has not in his place. He has a mistress who has a profound love for him, is entirely devoted to him, and who sends him all he wants in the way of silver, beverages and clothing.'

Then the man stopped speaking. The King was much surprised at what he had heard, but the Vizir, who had not missed a word of this conversation, had certainly made out, from what the man had said, that the negro was no other than his own.

The King requested the man to show him the house.

'If I show it you, what will you do?' asked the man.

'You will see what I shall do,' said the King. 'You will not be able to do anything,' replied the man, 'for it is a place which must be respected and feared. If you want to enter it by force you will risk death, for its master is redoubtable by means of his strength and courage.'

'Show me the place,' said the King, 'and have no fear.' The man answered, 'So be it as God will!'

He then rose, and walked before them. They followed him to a wide street, where he stopped in front of a house with lofty doors, the walls being on all sides high and inaccessible.

They examined the walls, looking for a place where they might be scaled, but with no result. To their surprise they found the house to be as close as a breastplate.

The King, turning to the man, asked him, 'What is your name?'

'Omar ben Isad,' he replied.

The King said to him, 'Omar, are you demented?'

'Yes, my brother,' answered he, 'if it so pleases God on high!' And turning to the King he added, 'May God assist you tonight!'

Then the King, addressing his attendants, said, 'Are you determined? Is there one amongst you who could scale these walls?'

'Impossible!' they all replied.

Then said the King, 'I myself will scale this wall, so please God on high! but by means of an expedient for which I require your assistance, and if you lend me the same I shall scale the wall, if it pleases God on high.'

They said, 'What is there to be done?'

'Tell me,' said the King, 'who is the strongest amongst you.' They replied, 'The Chief of the Police, who is your *Chaouch*.'

The King said, 'And who next?'

'The Commander of the Guards.'

'And after him, who?' asked the King.

'The Grand Vizir.'

Omar listened with astonishment. He knew now that it was the King, and his joy was great.

The King said, 'Who is there yet?'

Omar replied, 'I, O my master.'

The King said to him, 'O Omar, you have found out who we are; but do not betray our disguise, and you will be absolved from blame.'

'To hear is to obey,' said Omar.

The King then said to the *Chaouch*, 'Rest your hands against the wall so that your back projects.'

The *Chaouch* did so.

Then said the King to the commander of the guards, 'Mount upon the back of the *Chaouch*.' He did so, and stood with his feet on the other man's shoulders. Then the King ordered the Vizir to mount, and he got on the shoulders of the commander of the guards, and put his hands against the wall.

Then said the King, 'O Omar, mount upon the highest place!' And Omar, surprised by this expedient, cried, 'May God lend you his help, O our master, and assist you in your just enterprise!' He then got on to the shoulders of the *Chaouch*, and from there upon the back of the Commander of the Guards, and then upon that of the Vizir, and, standing upon the shoulders of the latter, he took the same position as the others. There was now only the King left.

Then the King said, 'In the name of God! and his blessing be with the prophet, upon whom be the mercy and salutation of God!' and, placing his hand upon the back of the *Chaouch*, he said, 'Have a moment's patience; if I succeed you will be compensated!' He then did the same with the others, until he got upon Omar's back, to whom he also said, 'O Omar, have a moment's patience with me, and I shall name you my private secretary. And, of all things, do not move!' Then, placing his feet upon Omar's shoulders, the King could with his hands grasp the terrace; and crying, 'In the name of God! may he pour his blessings upon the Prophet, on whom be the mercy and salutation of God!', he made a spring, and stood upon the terrace.

Then he said to his attendants, 'Descend now from each others shoulders!'

And they got down one after another, and they could not

help admiring the ingenious idea of the King, as well as the strength of the *Chaouch* who carried four men at once.

The King then began to look for a place for descending, but found no passage. He unrolled his turban, fixed one end with a single knot at the place where he was, and let himself down into the courtyard, which he explored until he found the portal in the middle of the house fastened with an enormous lock. The solidity of this lock, and the obstacle it created, gave him a disagreeable surprise. He said to himself, 'I am now in difficulty, but all comes from God; it was he who gave me the strength and the idea that brought me here; he will also provide the means for me to return to my companions.'

He then set himself to examine the place where he found himself, and counted the chambers one after another. He found seventeen chambers or rooms, furnished in different styles, with tapestries and velvet hangings of various colours, from the first to the last.

Examining all round, he saw a place raised by seven stair-steps, from which issued a great noise from voices. He went up to it, saying, 'O God! favour my project, and let me come safe and sound out of here.'

He mounted the first step, saying, 'In the name of God the compassionate and merciful!' Then he began to look at the steps, which were of variously coloured marble – black, red, white, yellow, green and other shades.

Mounting the second step, he said, 'He whom God helps is invincible!'

On the third step he said, 'With the aid of God the victory is near.'

And on the fourth, 'I have asked victory of God, who is the most puissant auxiliary.'

Finally he mounted the fifth, sixth, and seventh steps, invoking the Prophet (with whom be the mercy and salvation of God).

He then arrived at the curtain hanging at the entrance; it was of red brocade. From there he examined the room, which was bathed in light, filled with many chandeliers, and candles burning in golden sconces. In the middle of this saloon played a jet of musk-water. A table-cloth extended from end to end,[53] covered with sundry meats and fruits.

The saloon was provided with gilt furniture, the splendour of which dazzled the eye. In fact, everywhere, there were ornaments of all kinds.

On looking closer the King ascertained that round the table-cloth there were twelve maidens and seven women, all like moons; he was astonished at their beauty and grace. There were likewise with them seven negroes, and this sight filled him with surprise. His attention was above all attracted by a woman like the full moon, of perfect beauty, with black eyes, oval cheeks, and a lithe and graceful waist; she humbled the hearts of those who became enamoured of her.

Stupefied by her beauty, the King was as one stunned. He then said to himself, 'How is there any getting out of this place? O my spirit, do not give way to love !'

And continuing his inspection of the room, he perceived in the hands of those who were present, glasses filled with wine. They were drinking and eating, and it was easy to see they were overcome with drink.

While the King was pondering how to escape his embarrassment, he heard one of the women saying to one of her companions, calling her by name, 'Oh, so and so, rise and light a torch, so that we to can go to bed, for sleep is overpowering us. Come, light the torch, and let us retire to the other chamber.'

They rose and lifted up the curtain to leave the room. The King hid himself to let them pass; then, perceiving that they had left their chamber to do a thing necessary and obligatory in human kind, he took advantage of their absence, entered their apartment, and hid himself in a cupboard.

---

[53] The Arabs eat lying on carpets and cushions; they do not make use of tables, but have a table-cloth made of leather or stuff which is stretched on the ground for putting the dishes on. This table-cloth is called *sefra*.

Whilst he was thus in hiding the women returned and shut the doors. Their reason was obscured by the fumes of wine; they pulled off all their clothes and began to caress each other mutually.[54]

The King said to himself, 'Omar has told me true about this house of misfortune as an abyss of debauchery.'

When the women had fallen asleep the King rose, extinguished the light, undressed, and laid down between the two. He had taken care during their conversation to impress their names on his memory. So he was able to say to one of them, 'You, so and so, where have you put the door-keys?' speaking very low.

The woman answered, 'Go to sleep, you whore, the keys are in their usual place.'

The King said to himself, 'There is no might and strength but in God the Almighty and Benevolent!' and was much troubled.

And again he asked the woman about the keys, saying, 'Daylight is coming. I must open the doors. There is the sun. I am going to open the house.'

And she answered, 'The keys are in the usual place. Why do you thus bother me? Sleep, I say, till it is day.'

And again the King said to himself, 'There is no might and strength but in God the Almighty and Benevolent, and surely if it were not for the fear of God I should run my sword through her.' Then he began again, 'Oh, you, so and so!'

She said, 'What do you want?'

'I am uneasy,' said the King, 'about the keys; tell me where they are?'

And she answered, 'You hussy! Does your vulva itch for coition? Cannot you do without for a single night? Look! the Vizir's wife has withstood all the entreaties of the negro, and repelled him since six months! Go, the keys are in the negro's pocket. Do not say to him, "Give me the keys;" but say, "Give me your member." You know his name is Dorérame.'

[54] The text says literally: 'They set to work on each other mutually.'

The King was now silent, for he knew what to do. He waited a short time till the woman was asleep; then he dressed himself in her clothes, and concealed his sword under them; his face he hid under a veil of red silk. Thus dressed he looked like other women. Then he opened the door, stole softly out, and placed himself behind the curtains of the saloon entrance. He saw only some people sitting there; the remainder were asleep.

The King made the following silent prayer, 'O my soul, let me follow the right way, and let all those people among whom I find myself be stunned with drunkenness, so that they cannot know the King from his subjects, and God give me strength.'

He then entered the saloon saying: 'In the name of God!' and he tottered towards the bed of the negro as if drunk. The negroes and the women took him to be the woman whose attire he had taken.

Dorérame had a great desire to have his pleasure with that woman, and when he saw her sit down by the bed he thought that she had broken her sleep to come to him, perhaps for love games. So he said, 'Oh, you, so and so, undress and get into my bed, I shall soon be back.'

The King said to himself, 'There is no might and strength but in the High God, the Benevolent!' Then he searched for the keys in the clothes and pockets of the negro, but found nothing. He said, 'God's will be done!' Then raising his eyes, he saw a high window; he reached up with his arm, and found gold embroidered garments there; he slipped his hands into the pockets, and, oh, surprise! he found the keys. He examined them and counted seven, corresponding to the number of the doors of the house, and in his joy, he exclaimed, 'God, be praised and glorified!' Then he said, 'I can only get out of here by a ruse.' Then feigning sickness, and appearing as if he wanted to vomit violently, he held his hand before his mouth, and hurried to the centre of the courtyard. The negro said to him, 'God bless you! oh, so and so! any other woman would have been sick into the bed!'

The King then went to the inner door of the house, and opened it; he closed it behind him, and so from one door to the other, till he came to the seventh, which opened upon the street. Here he found his companions again, who had been in great anxiety, and who asked him what he had seen?

Then said the King: 'This is not the time to answer. Let us go into this house with the blessing of God and with his help.'

They resolved to be upon their guard, there being in the house seven negroes, twelve maidens, and seven women, beautiful as moons.

The Vizir asked the King, 'What garments are these?' And the King answered, 'Be silent; without them I should never have got the keys.,

He then went to the chamber where were the two women, with whom he had been lying, took off the clothes in which he was dressed, and resumed his own, taking good care of his sword. Repairing to the saloon, where the negroes and the women were, he and his companions ranged themselves behind the door-curtain.

After having looked into the saloon, they said, 'Amongst all these women there is none more beautiful than the one seated on the elevated cushion!' The King said, 'I reserve her for myself, if she does not belong to someone else.'

While they were examining the interior of the saloon, Dorérame descended from the bed, and after him one of those beautiful women. Then another negro got on the bed with another woman, and so on till the seventh. They rode them in this way, one after the other, excepting the beautiful woman mentioned above, and the maidens. Each of these women appeared to mount upon the bed with marked reluctance, and descended, after the coition was finished, with her head bent down.

The negroes, however, were lusting after, and pressing one after the other, the beautiful woman. But she spurned them all, saying, 'I shall never consent to it, and as to these virgins, I take them also under my protection.'

Dorérame then rose and went up to her, holding in his hands his member in full erection, stiff as a pillar.[55] He hit her with it on the face and head, saying, 'Six times this night I have pressed you to cede to my desires, and you always refuse; but now I must have you, even this night.'

When the woman saw the stubbornness of the negro and the state of drunkenness he was in, she tried to soften him by promises. 'Sit down here by me,' she said, 'and tonight thy desires shall be contented.'

The negro sat down near to her with his member still erect as a column. The King could scarcely master his surprise.

Then the woman began to sing the following verses, intoning them from the bottom of her heart:

I prefer a young man for coition, and him only;
He is full of courage – he is my sole ambition,
His member is strong to deflower the virgin,
And richly proportioned in all its dimensions;
It has a head like to a brazier.
Enormous, and none like it in creation;
Strong it is and hard, with the head rounded off.
It is always ready for action and does not die down;
It never sleeps, owing to the violence of its love.
It sighs to enter my vulva, and sheds tears on my belly;
It asks not for help, not being in want of any;
It has no need of an ally, and stands alone the greatest fatigues,
And nobody can be sure of what will result from its efforts.
Full of vigour and life, it bores into my vagina,
And it works about there in action constant and splendid.
First from the front to the back, and then from the right to the left;
Now it is crammed hard in by vigorous pressure,
Now it rubs its head on the orifice of my vagina.
And he strokes my back, my stomach, my sides,
Kisses my cheeks, and anon begins to suck at my lips.
He embraces me close, and makes me roll on the bed,
And between his arms I am like a corpse without life.
Every part of my body receives in turn his love-bites,
And he covers me with kisses of fire;
When he sees me in heat he quickly comes to me,
Then he opens my thighs and kisses my belly,

[55] The Arabian text has it literally, *Ou aïrouhou kaïme bine ïadihi ki el eûmoud*. *Eûmoud* signifies 'pillar, column.'

And puts his tool in my hand to make it knock at my door.
Soon he is in the cave, and I feel pleasure approaching.
He shakes me and trills me, and hotly we both are working,
And he says, 'Receive my seed!' and I answer, 'Oh give it beloved one!
It shall be welcome to me, you light of my eyes!
Oh, you man of all men, who fillest me with pleasure.
Oh, you soul of my soul, go on with fresh vigour,
For you must not yet withdraw it from me; leave it there,
And this day will then be free of all sorrow.'
He has sworn to God to have me for seventy nights,
And what he wished for he did, in the way of kisses and embraces, during all those nights.

When she had finished, the King, in great surprise, said, 'How lascivious has God made this woman.' And turning to his companions, 'There is no doubt that this woman has no husband, and has not been debauched, for, certainly that negro is in love with her, and she has nevertheless repulsed him.'

Omar ben Isad took the word, 'This is true, O King! Her husband has been now away for nearly a year, and many men have endeavoured to debauch her, but she has resisted.'

The King asked, 'Who is her husband?' And his companions answered, 'She is the wife of the son of your father's Vizir.'

The King replied, 'You speak true; I have indeed heard it said that the son of my father's Vizir had a wife without fault, endowed with beauty and perfection and of exquisite shape; not adulterous and innocent of debauchery.'

'This is the same woman,' said they.

The King said, 'No matter how, but I must have her,' and turning to Omar, he added, 'Where, amongst these women, is your mistress?' Omar answered, 'I do not see her, O King!' Upon which the King said, 'Have patience, I will show her to you.' Omar was quite surprised to find that the King knew so much. 'And this then is the negro Dorérame?' asked the King. 'Yes, and he is a slave of mine,' answered the Vizir. 'Be silent, this is not the time to speak,' said the King.

While this discourse was going on, the negro Dorérame, still desirous of obtaining the favours of that lady, said to her, 'I am tired of your lies, O Beder el Bedour' (full moon of the full moons), for so she called herself.

The King said, 'He who called her so called her by her true name, for she is the full moon of the full moons, afore God!'

However, the negro wanted to draw the woman away with him, and hit her in the face.

The King, mad with jealousy, and with his heart full of ire, said to the Vizir, 'Look what your negro is doing! By God! he shall die the death of a villain, and I shall make an example of him, and a warning to those who would imitate him!'

At that moment the King heard the lady say to the negro, 'You are betraying your master the Vizir with his wife, and now you betray her, in spite of your intimacy with her and the favours she grants to you.[56] And surely she loves you passionately, and you are pursuing another woman!'

The King said to the Vizir, 'Listen, and do not speak a word.'

The lady then rose and returned to the place where she had been before, and began to recite:

> Oh, men! listen to what I say on the subject of woman,[57]
> Her thirst for coition is written between her eyes.
> Do not put trust in her vows, even were she the Sultan's daughter.
> Woman's malice is boundless; not even the King of kings
> Would suffice to subdue it, whate'er be his might.
> Men, take heed and shun the love of woman!
> Do not say, 'Such a one is my well beloved;'
> Do not say, 'She is my life's companion.'
> If I deceive you, then say my words are untruths.
> As long as she is with you in bed, you have her love,
> But a woman's love is not enduring, believe me.
> Lying upon her breast, you are her love-treasure;
> Whilst the coition goes on, you have her love, poor fool!

[56] 'You are betraying your master,' etc. By this phrase is rendered a passage in the text which runs, 'You betray the salt. and you betray the wife of the Vizir.' 'To betray the salt' is a figurative phrase in allusion to the Oriental usage of hospitality in offering salt, and signifies 'betraying the host, the master, the hand that nourishes.'

[57] 'Woman's nature is represented to us by the moon.' – (*Rabelais*, book iii, chap. xxxii.)

> But, anon, she looks upon you as a fiend;
> And this is a fact undoubted and certain.
> The wife receives the slave in the bed of the master,
> And the serving-men allay upon her their lust.
> Certain it is, such conduct is not to be praised and honoured.
> But the virtue of women is frail and changeful,
> And the man thus deceived is looked upon with contempt.
> Therefore a man with a heart should not put trust in a woman.

At these words the Vizir began to cry, but the King bade him to be quiet. Then the negro recited the following verses in response to those of the lady:

> We negroes have had our fill of women,
> We fear not their tricks, however subtle they be.
> Men confide in us with regard to what they cherish.[58]
> This is no lie, remember, but is the truth, as you know.
> Oh, you women all! for sure you have no patience when the virile
>   member you are wanting,
> For in the same resides your life and death;
> It is the end and all of your wishes, secret or open.
> If your choler and ire are aroused against your husbands,
> They appease you simply by introducing their members.
> Your religion resides in your vulva, and the manly member is your soul.
> Such you will always find is the nature of woman.

With that, the negro threw himself upon the woman, who pushed him back.

At this moment, the King felt his heart oppressed; he drew his sword, as did his companions, and they entered the room. The negroes and women saw nothing but brandished swords.

One of the negroes rose, and rushed upon the King and his companions, but the *Chaouch* severed with one blow his head from his body. The King cried, 'God's blessing upon you! Your arm is not withered and your mother has not borne a weakling. You have struck down your enemies, and paradise shall be your dwelling and place of rest!'

Another negro got up and aimed a blow at the *Chaouch*, which broke the sword of the *Chaouch* in twain. It had been a

---

[58] This verse alludes to the fact that negroes, as domestics, are considered as an inferior class, who are allowed to come near women, as incapable of making an impression.

beautiful weapon, and the *Chaouch*, on seeing it ruined, broke out into the most violent passion; he seized the negro by the arm, lifted him up, and threw him against the wall, breaking his bones. Then the King cried, 'God is great. He has not dried up your hand. Oh, what a *Chaouch*! God grant you his blessing.'

The negroes, when they saw this, were cowed and silent, and the King, master now of their lives, said, 'The man that lifts his hand only, shall lose his head!' And he commanded that the remaining five negroes should have their hands tied behind their backs.

This having been done, he turned to Beder el Bedour and asked her, 'Whose wife are you, and who is this negro?'

She then told him on that subject what he had heard already from Omar. And the King thanked her, saying, 'May God give you his blessing.' He then asked her, 'How long can a woman patiently do without coition?' She seemed amazed, but the King said, 'Speak, and do not be abashed.'

She then answered, 'A well-born lady of high origin can remain for six months without; but a lowly woman of no race nor high blood, who does not respect herself when she can lay her hand upon a man, will have him upon her; his stomach and his member will know her vagina.'

Then said the King, pointing to one of the women, 'Who is this one?' She answered, 'This is the wife of the *Kadi*.' 'And this one?' 'The wife of the second Vizir.' 'And this?' 'The wife of the chief of the *Muftis*.' 'And that one?' 'The Treasurer's.' 'And those two women that are in the other room?' She answered, 'They have received the hospitality of the house, and one of them was brought here yesterday by an old woman; the negro has so far not got possession of her.'

Then said Omar, 'This is the one I spoke to you about, O my master.'

'And the other woman? To whom does she belong?' said the King.

'She is the wife of the Amine[59] of the carpenters,' answered she.

Then said the King, 'And these girls, who are they?'

She answered, 'This one is the daughter of the clerk of the treasury; this other one the daughter of the Mohtesib,[60] the third is the daughter of the Bouab,[61] the next one the daughter of the Amine of the Moueddin;[62] that one the daughter of the colour-keeper.[63] At the invitation of the King, she passed them thus all in review.

The King then asked for the reason of so many women being brought together there.

Beder el Bedour replied, 'O master of ours, the negro knows no other passions than for coition and good wine. He keeps making love night and day, and his member rests only when he himself is asleep.'[64]

The King asked further, 'What does he live upon?'

She said, 'Upon yolks of eggs fried in fat and swimming in

[59] The title Amine corresponds to our councillor; syndic.
[60] The Mohtesib is a commissioner of the police, charged with surveying weights and measures.
[61] Bouab signifies an usher.
[62] The Moueddin are the criers, who call, from the top of the Mosques, the true believers to prayers.
[63] The Oriental sovereigns having a great number of flags, standards, etc., which are carried before them on the occasions of state ceremonials, and which they take with them to their wars, the keeper of those colours is a man of importance.
[64] Whilst on the subject of negroes, it seems pertinent here to quote from a footnote to Burton's Arabian Nights (Vol. 1, page 6, note 1): 'Debauched women prefer Negroes on account of the size of their parts. I measured one man in Somaliland who, when quiescent, numbered nearly six inches. This is a characteristic of the negro race and of African animals. . . . Moreover, these imposing parts do not increase proportionally during erection; consequently, the "deed of kind" takes a much longer time and adds greatly to the woman's enjoyment. In my time no honest Hindi Moslem would take his women-folk to Zanzibar on account of the huge attractions and enormous temptations there and thereby offered to them. Upon the subject of Imsák=retention of semen and 'prolongation of pleasure' I shall find it necessary to say more.'—Regarding this remark see my Introduction to the present volume, page 30. Havelock Ellis, in his Studies, makes various comments on the preference of certain types of debauched white women for over-developed men, though these are by no means necessarily coloured. (A.H.W.)

honey, and upon white bread; he drinks nothing but old muscatel wine.'

The King said, 'Who has brought these women here, who, all of them, belong to officials of the State?'

She replied, 'O master of ours, he has in his service an old woman who has had the run of the houses in the town; she chooses and brings to him any woman of superior beauty and perfection; but she serves him only against good consideration in silver, dresses, etc., precious stones, rubies, and other objects of value.'

'And whence does the negro get that silver?' asked the King. The lady remaining silent, he added, 'Give me some information, please.'

She signified with a sign from the corner of her eye that he had got it all from the wife of the Grand Vizir.

The King understood her, and continued, 'O Beder el Bedour! I have faith and confidence in you, and your testimony will have in my eyes the value of that of the two *Adels*.[65] Speak to me without reserve as to what concerns yourself.'

She answered him, 'I have not been touched, and however long this might have lasted the negro would not have had his desire satisfied.'

'Is this so?' asked the King.

She replied, 'It is so!' She had understood what the King wanted to say, and the King had seized the meaning of her words.

'Has the negro respected *my* honour? Inform me about that,' said the King.

she answered, 'They are his companions. After he had quite surfeited himself with the women he had caused to be brought to far; but if God had spared his days there is no certainty that he would not have tried to soil what he should have respected.'

The King having asked her then who those negroes were,

---

[65] The two *Adels* (*Adeline*) are the two sworn witnesses who assist the Cadi when he sits in judgment.

she answered, 'They are his companions. After he had quite surfeited himself with the women he had caused to be brought to him, he handed them over to them, as you have seen. If it were not for the protection of a woman where would that man be?'

Then spoke the King, 'O Beder el Bedour, why did not your husband ask my help against this oppression? Why did you not complain?'

She replied, 'O King of the time, O beloved Sultan, O master of numerous armies and allies! As regards my husband I was so far unable to inform him of my lot; as to myself I have nothing to say but what you know by the verses I sang just now. I have given advice to men about women from the first verse to the last.'

The King said, 'O Beder el Bedour! I like you, I have put the question to you in the name of the chosen Prophet (the benediction and mercy of God be with him!). Inform me of everything; you have nothing to fear; I give you the *aman*[66] complete. Has this negro not enjoyed you? For I presume that none of you were out of reach of his attempts and had her honour safe.'

She replied, 'O King of our time, in the name of your high rank and your power! Look! He, about whom you ask me, I would not have accepted him as a legitimate husband; how could I have consented to grant him the favour of an illicit love?'

The King said, 'You appear to be sincere, but the verses I heard you sing have roused doubts in my soul.'

She replied, 'I had three motives for employing that language. Firstly, I was at that moment in heat, like a young mare; secondly, Eblis had excited my natural parts; and lastly, I wanted to quiet the negro and make him have patience, so that he should grant me some delay and leave me in peace until God would deliver me of him.'

The King said, 'Do you speak seriously?' She was silent. Then the King cried, 'O Beder el Bedour, you alone shall be pardoned!' She understood that it was she only that the King would spare

[66] The *aman*, that is the pardon, absolution, protection; this is a compact or treaty of indemnity.

from the punishment of death. He then cautioned her that she must keep the secret, and said he wanted to leave now.

Then all the women and virgins approached Beder el Bedour and implored her, saying, 'Intercede for us, for you have power over the King;' and they shed tears over her hands, and in despair threw themselves down.

Beder el Bedour then called the King back, as he was going, and said to him, 'O our master! you have not granted me any favour yet.' 'How,' said he, 'I have sent for a beautiful mule for you; you will mount her and come with us. As for these women, they must all of them die.'

She then said, 'O our master! I ask you and conjure you to authorise me to make a stipulation which you will accept.' The King made oath that he would fulfil it. Then she said, 'I ask as a gift the pardon of all these women and of all these maidens. Their deaths would moreover throw the most terrible consternation over the whole town.'

The King said, 'There is no might nor power but in God, the merciful!' He then ordered the negroes to be taken out and beheaded. The only exception he made was with the negro Dorérame,[67] who was enormously stout and had a neck like a bull. They cut off his ears, nose, and lips; likewise his virile member, which they put into his mouth, and then hung him on a gallows.

Then the King ordered the seven doors of the house to be closed, and returned to his palace.

[67] Dorérame, in the Carrington edition, becomes 'Dhurgam'. His verses, as all verses throughout that edition, are translated into rhyming English metres. Unfortunately most of them exaggerate the subject matter, and (this is one of the faults of the Carrington version) become unnecessarily obscene, and therefore unquotable. The method adopted throughout the Kama Shastra edition (i.e. a literal prose rendering, set in smaller type) is probably best adapted to give an exact idea of the sense of the original Arabic. Dhurgam's verses, in the Carrington edition (page 249), open thus:

'We slaves that have the pretty ones in charge
  Can have as many women as we like;
We care not for our master's cunning wiles,
  However great the power they have to strike.' (*etc.*) (A.H.W.)

At sunrise he sent a mule to Beder el Bedour, in order to let her be brought to him. He made her dwell with him, and found her to be excelling all those who excel.

Then the King caused the wife of Omar ben Isad to be restored to him, and he made him his private secretary. After which he ordered the Vizir to repudiate his wife. He did not forget the *Chaouch* and the Commander of the Guards, to whom he made large presents, as he had promised, using for that purpose the negro's hoards. He sent the son of his father's Vizir to prison. He also caused the old go-between to be brought before him, and asked her, 'Give me all the particulars about the conduct of the negro, and tell me whether it was well done to bring in that way women to men.' She answered, 'This is the trade of nearly all old women.' He then had her executed, as well as all old women who followed that trade, and thus cut off in his State the tree of panderism at the root, and burnt the trunk.

He besides sent back to their families all the women and girls, and bade them repent in the name of God.

This story presents but a small part of the tricks and stratagems used by women against their husbands.

The moral of the tale is, that a man who falls in love with a woman imperils himself, and exposes himself to the greatest troubles.

CHAPTER III

About Men who are to be Held in Contempt

KNOW, O MY BROTHER (to whom God be merciful), that
a man who is misshapen, of coarse appearance, and whose
member is short, thin and flabby, is contemptible in the
eyes of women.

When such a man has a bout with a woman, he does not do
his business with vigour and in a manner to give her enjoyment. He lays himself down upon her without previous toying,
he does not kiss her, nor twine himself round her; he does not
bite her, nor suck her lips, nor tickle her.

He gets upon her before she has begun to long for pleasure,
and then he introduces with infinite trouble a member soft and
nerveless. Scarcely has he commenced when he is already done
for; he makes one or two movements, and then sinks upon the
woman's breast to spend his sperm; and that is the most he can
do. This done he with-draws his affair, and makes all haste to
get down again from her.

Such a man—as was said by a writer—is quick in ejaculation
and slow as to erection; after the trembling, which follows the
ejaculation of the seed, his chest is heavy and his sides ache.

Qualities like these are no recommendation with women.
Despicable also is the man who is false in his words; who does
not fulfil the promise he has made; who never speaks without
telling lies, and who conceals from his wife all his doings,
except the adulterous exploits which he commits.

Women cannot esteem such men, as they cannot procure them any enjoyment.

It is said that a man of the name of Abbés, whose member was extremely small and slight, had a very corpulent wife, whom he could not contrive to satisfy in coition, so that she soon began to complain to her female friends about it.

This woman possessed a considerable fortune, whilst Abbés was very poor; and when he wanted anything, she was sure not to let him have what he wanted.

One day he went to see a wise man, and submitted his case to him.

The sage told him: 'If you had a fine member you might dispose of her fortune. Do you not know that women's religion is in their vulvas? But I will prescribe you a remedy which will do away with your troubles.'

Abbés lost no time in making up the remedy according to the recipe of the wise man, and after he had used it his member grew to be long and thick. When his wife saw it in that state she was surprised; but it was still better when he made her feel in the matter of enjoyment quite another thing than she had been accustomed to experience; he began in fact to work her with his tool in quite a remarkable manner, to such a point that she trembled and sighed and sobbed and cried out during the operation.

As soon as the wife found in her husband such eminently good qualities she gave him her fortune, and placed her person and all she had at his disposal.

CHAPTER IV

About Women who are to be Held in Contempt

KNOW, O VIZIR (to whom God be merciful), that women differ in their natural dispositions: there are women who are worthy of all praise; and there are, on the other hand, women who only merit contempt.

The woman who merits the contempt of men is ugly and garrulous; her hair is woolly, her forehead projecting, her eyes are small and blear, her nose is enormous, the lips lead-coloured, the mouth large, the cheeks wrinkled and she shows gaps in her teeth; her cheekbones shine purple, and she sports bristles on her chin; her head sits on a meagre neck, with very much developed tendons; her shoulders are contracted and her chest is narrow, with flabby pendulous breasts, and her belly is like an empty leather-bottle, with the navel standing out like a heap of stones; her flanks are shaped like arcades; the bones of her spinal column may be counted; there is no flesh upon her croup; her vulva is large and cold.

Finally, such a woman has large knees and feet,[68] big hands and emaciated legs.

A woman with such blemishes can give no pleasure to men in general, and least of all to him who is her husband or who enjoys her favours.

The man who approaches a woman like that with his member

---

[68] 'Feet like a guitar.' (*Rabelais*, book iv, chap. xxxi.)

in erection will find it presently soft and relaxed, as though he was only close to a beast of burden. May God keep us from a woman of that description!

Contemptible likewise is the woman who is constantly laughing out; for, as it was said by an author, 'If you see a woman who is always laughing, fond of gaming and jesting, always running to her neighbours, meddling with matters that are no concern of hers, plaguing her husband with constant complaints, leaguing herself with other women against him, playing the grand lady, accepting gifts from everybody, know that that woman is a whore without shame.'

And again to be despised is the woman of a sombre, frowning nature, and one who is prolific in talk; the woman who is light-headed in her relations with men, or contentious, or fond of tittle-tattle and unable to keep her husband's secrets, or who is malicious. The woman of a malicious nature talks only to tell lies; if she makes a promise she does so only to break it, and if anybody confides in her, she betrays him; she is debauched, thievish, a scold, coarse and violent; she cannot give good advice; she is always occupied with the affairs of other people, and with such as bring harm, and is always on the watch for frivolous news; she is fond of repose, but not of work; she uses unbecoming words in addressing a Mussulman, even to her husband; invectives are always at her tongue's end; she exhales a bad odour which infects you, and sticks to you even after you have left her.

And not less contemptible is she who talks to no purpose, who is a hypocrite and does no good act; she, who, when her husband asks her to fulfil the conjugal office, refuses to listen to his demand; the woman who does not assist her husband in his affairs; and finally, she who plagues him with unceasing complaints and tears.

A woman of that sort, seeing her husband irritated or in trouble does not share his affliction; on the contrary, she laughs and jests all the more, and does not try to drive away his ill-humour by endearments. She is more prodigal with her person to other men than to her husband; it is not for his sake that she adorns herself, and it is not to please him that she tries to look well. Far from that; with him she is very untidy, and does not mind letting him see things and habits about her person which must be repugnant to him. Lastly, she never uses either *Atsmed* nor *Souak*.[69]

No happiness can be hoped for a man with such a wife. God keep us from such a one!

[69] *Atsmed* is antimony, of which an eye-salve is made. The women blacken the inside of the eyelids with it, to make the eyes appear larger and more brilliant.

CHAPTER V

Relating to the Act of Generation

K NOW, O VIZIR (and God protect you!), that if you wish
for coition, in joining the woman you should not have
your stomach loaded with food and drink, only in that
condition will your cohabitation be wholesome and good. If your
stomach is full, only harm can come of it to both of you; you
will have threatening symptoms of apoplexy and gout, and the
least evil that may result from it will be the inability of passing
your urine, or weakness of sight.

Let your stomach then be free from excessive food and drink,
and you need not apprehend any illness.

Before setting to work with your wife excite her with toying,
so that the copulation will finish to your mutual satisfaction.[70]

[70] Regarding love-play, see Van de Velde, *Ideal Marriage*. Havelock
Ellis has much to say regarding this all-important subject in the masterly
chapter entitled 'The Art of Love,' in his *Studies*, volume VI (*Sex in
Relation to Society* (volume IV in the Random House edition). He
develops the theme at length in his essay on *The Play-Function of Sex*
(in *Little Essays of Love and Virtue*), where he says: 'While the husband
is content with a mere simulacrum and pretense of the erotic life, the
wife often (has) none at all. Few people realise – few indeed have the
knowledge or the opportunity to realise – how much women thus lose,
alike in the means to fulfil their own lives and in the power to help
others.' (Mentor edition, New York (under title of *On Life & Sex*), 1957,
page 83). Kinsey, likewise, discusses various aspects of the matter.—Be
that as it may, unless there is love between a couple, or at least mutual
attraction, love-play tends to lose something of its potency. In the case
of one partner being revolted by the other, then such preliminaries may
well become equally revolting to the sensibilities of that partner. Love is
an art, the sexual act is an art, and there is no magic panacea, no

Thus it will be well to play with her before you introduce your verge and accomplish the cohabitation. You will excite her by kissing her cheeks, sucking her lips and nibbling at her breasts. You will lavish kisses on her navel and thighs, and titillate the lower parts. Bite at her arms, and neglect no part of her body; cling close to her bosom, and show her your love and submission. Interlace your legs with hers, and press her in your arms, for, as the poet has said:

> Under her neck my right hand has served her for a cushion,
> And to draw her to me
> I have sent out my left hand,
> Which bore her up as a bed.

When you are close to a woman, and you see her eyes getting dim, and hear her, yearning for coition, heave deep sighs, then let your and her yearning be joined into one, and let your lubricity rise to the highest point; for this will be the moment most favourable to the game of love. The pleasure which the woman then feels will be extreme; as for yourself, you will cherish her all the more, and she will continue her affection for you, for it has been said:

If you see a woman heaving deep sighs, with her lips getting red and her eyes languishing, when her mouth half opens and her movements grow heedless; when she appears to be disposed to go to sleep, vacillating in her steps and prone to yawn, know that this is the moment for coition; and if you there and then make your way into her you will procure for her an unquestionable treat. You yourself will find the mouth of her womb clasping your article, which is undoubtedly the crowning pleasure for both, for this before everything begets affection and love.

enchanted set of golden rules which will miraculously open the door to success. Books such as the *Garden* may do much to help, but their teachings must be modified to meet the individual case; and each man and woman must modify according to their own needs, circumstances, religion, and temperament. (A.H.W.)

The following precepts, coming from a profound connoisseur in love affairs, are well known:

Woman is like a fruit, which will not yield its sweetness until you rub it between your hands. Look at the basil plant; if you do not rub it warm with your fingers it will not emit any scent. Do you not know that the amber, unless it be handled and warmed, keeps hidden within its pores the aroma contained in it. It is the same with woman. If you do not animate her with your toying, intermixed with kissing, nibbling and touching, you will not obtain from her what you are wishing; you will feel no enjoyment when you share her couch, and you will waken in her heart neither inclination nor affection, nor love for you; all her qualities will remain hidden.

It is reported that a man, having asked a woman what means were the most likely to create affection in the female heart, with respect to the pleasures of coition, received the following answer:

O you who question me, those things which develop the taste for coition are the toyings and touches which precede it, and then the close embrace at the moment of ejaculation!

Believe me, the kisses, nibblings, suction of the lips, the close embrace, the visits of the mouth to the nipples of the bosom, and the sipping of the fresh saliva, these are the things to render affection lasting.

In acting thus, the two orgasms take place simultaneously, and enjoyment comes to the man and woman at the same moment. Then the man feels the womb grasping his member, which gives to each of them the most exquisite pleasure.

This it is which gives birth to love, and if matters have not been managed this way the woman has not had her full share of pleasure, and the delights of the womb are wanting. Know that the woman will not feel her desires satisfied, and will not love her rider unless he is able to act up to her womb; but when the womb is made to enter into action she will feel the most violent love for her cavalier, even if he be unsightly in appearance.

Then do all you can to provoke a simultaneous discharge of the two spermal fluids; herein lies the secret of love.[71]

One of the savants who have occupied themselves with this subject has thus related the confidences which one of them made to him:

O you men, one and all, who are soliciting the love of woman and her affection, and who wish that sentiment in her heart to be of an enduring nature, toy with her previous to coition; prepare her for enjoyment, and neglect nothing to attain that end. Explore her with the greater assiduity, and, entirely occupied with her, let nothing else engage your thoughts. Do not let the moment propitious for pleasure pass away; that moment will be when you see her eyes humid, half open. Then go to work, but, remember, not till your kisses and toyings have taken effect.

After you have got the woman into a proper state of excitement, O men! put your member into her, and, if you then observe the proper movements, she will experience a pleasure which will satisfy all her desires.

Lie on her breast, rain kisses on her cheeks, and let not your member quit her vagina. Push for the mouth of her womb. This will crown your labour.

If, by God's favour, you have found this delight, take good care not to with-draw your member, but let it remain there, and imbibe an endless pleasure! Listen to the sighs

[71] It was long thought that the woman, like the man, ejected a 'spermal fluid' at the moment of orgasm. This, of course, has been proved not to be the case. She may, however, under the influence of excitement, produce a copious libation of 'lubricating' fluid; and is also capable of experiencing the sensations of orgasm. Individuals vary from one to another as regards the intensity of this. See, for example, *The Encyclopaedia of Sex Practice* (partly under the editorship of Norman Haire, Ch. M., M.B.), London, no date (*circa* 1940-43, and recently reprinted). (A.H.W.)

and heavy breathing of the woman. They witness the violence of the bliss you have given her.

And after the enjoyment is over, and your amorous struggle has come to an end, be careful not to get up at once, but with-draw your member cautiously. Remain close to the woman, and lie down on the right side of the bed that witnessed your enjoyment. You will find this pleasant, and you will not be like a fellow who mounts the woman after the fashion of a mule, without any regard to refinement, and who, after the emission, hastens to get his member out and to rise. Avoid such manners, for they rob the woman of all her lasting delight.

In short, the true lover of coition will not fail to observe all that I have recommended; for, from the observance of my recommendations will result the pleasure of the woman, and these rules comprise everything essential in that respect.

God has made everything for the best !

CHAPTER VI

Concerning Everything that is Favourable to the Act of Coition

KNOW, O VIZIR (God be good to you!), if you would have pleasant coition, which ought to give an equal share of happiness to the two combatants and be satisfactory to both, you must first of all toy with the woman, excite her with kisses, by nibbling and sucking her lips, by caressing her neck and cheeks. Turn her over in the bed, now on her back, now on her stomach, till you see by her eyes that the time for pleasure is near, as I have mentioned in the preceding chapter, and certainly I have not been sparing with my observations thereupon.

Then when you observe the lips of a woman to tremble and get red, and her eyes to become languishing, and her sighs to become quicker, know that she is hot for coition; then get between her thighs, so that your member can enter into her vagina. If you follow my advice, you will enjoy a pleasant embrace, which will give you the greatest satisfaction, and leave with you a delicious remembrance.

Someone has said:

If you desire coition, place the woman on the ground, cling closely to her bosom, with her lips close to yours; then clasp her to you, suck her breath, bite her; kiss her breasts, her stomach, her flanks, press her close in your arms, so as to make her faint with pleasure; when you see her so far gone, then push your member into her. If you have done as I said, the enjoyment will come to both of you simultaneously. This it is which makes the pleasure of the woman so sweet. But if you neglect my advice the woman will not be satisfied and you will not have procured her any pleasure.

The coition being finished, do not get up at once, but come down softly on her right side, and if she has conceived, she will bear a male child, if it please God on high![72]

Sages and Savants (may God grant to all his forgiveness!) have said:

If anyone placing his hand upon the vulva of a woman that is with child pronounces the following words: 'In the name of God! may he grant salutation and mercy to his Prophet (salutation and mercy be with him). Oh! my God! I pray to thee in the name of the Prophet to let a boy issue from this conception,' it will come to pass by the will of God, and in consideration for our lord Mohammed, (the salutation and grace of God be with him), the woman will be delivered of a boy.[73]

Do not drink rain-water directly after copulation, because this beverage weakens the kidneys.

If you want to repeat the coition, perfume yourself with sweet scents, then close with the woman, and you will arrive at a happy result.

Do not let the woman perform the act of coition mounted upon you, for fear that in that position some drops of her seminal fluid might enter the canal of your verge and cause a sharp urethritis.[74]

[72] This, of course, is nonsense, but is an interesting example of the sexual superstition of the Arab. (A.H.W.)

[73] Another Arab superstition. At that period they knew nothing about chromosomes. One wonders, however, if, prior to conception, or near the moment of conception, some kind of psychokinetic influence might not, in some cases, be possible. (A.H.W.)

[74] Although the dictionary gives no clue with respect to this illness, I thought it well, in conformity with the information I took, to call it sharp urethritis, a disease which is vulgarly called gonorrhoea with stricture.

Do not work hard directly after coition as this might affect your health adversely, but go to rest for some time.

Do not wash your verge directly after having with-drawn it from the vagina of the woman, until the irritation has gone down somewhat; then wash it and its opening carefully. Other-wise, do not wash your member frequently. Do not leave the vulva directly after the emission, as this may cause canker.[75]

Sundry Positions for the Coitus

The ways of doing it to women are numerous and variable. And now is the time to make known to you the different positions which are usual.

God, the magnificent, has said:

'Women are your field. Go upon your field as you like.'[76] According to your wish you can choose the position you like best, provided, of course, that coition takes place in the spot destined for it, that is, in the vulva.

Manner the first – Make the woman lie upon her back, with her thighs raised, then, getting between her legs, introduce your member into her. Pressing your toes to the ground, you can

[75] Although I have translated the word with canker it may, according to the dictum of some practitioners, signify also an affection that is known under the name of *sefia*, otherwise putrefaction, which is simply gonor-rhoea.—See also the original note 74 (page 128, above). Gonorrhoea cannot of course, be contracted, unless one comes into contact with the infection itself. Nor does a woman emit 'seminal fluid' as Nefzawi states. What he refers to is simply the female lubrication; or, perhaps, in certain cases, that female affection known as leucorrhoea ('the whites'). There was some confusion in the medical ideas of those times. If no disease is present in the woman, all that could affect a man after (probably excessive) coitus would be a harmless urethral catarrh or blenorrhoea, which is certainly not gonorrhoeal. In some men even a chill may bring on a non-specific urethritis, without any connection with a woman. Only a doctor can tell the difference between the dangerous and the harmless disturb-ances. (Original note expanded by A.H.W.)

[76] This passage is an extract from the 223rd verse, chap. ii of the Koran. The same runs: 'The women are your field. Go upon your field as you list, but do previously some good deed for your soul's sake. Fear God and be mindful of the day when you shall be in his presence.'

I

rummage her in a convenient, measured way.[77] This is a good position for a man with a long verge.

Manner the second – If your member is a short one, let the woman lie on her back, lift her legs into the air, so that her right leg be near her right ear, and the left one near her left ear, and in this posture, with her buttocks lifted up, her vulva will project forward. Then put in your member.

Manner the third – Let the woman stretch herself upon the ground, and place yourself between her thighs; then putting one of her legs upon your shoulder, and the other under your arm, near the armpit, get into her.

Manner the fourth – Let her lie down, and put her legs on your shoulders; in this position your member will just face her vulva, which must not touch the ground. And then introduce your member.

Manner the fifth – Let her lie down on her side, then lie yourself down by her on your side, and getting between her thighs, put your member into her vagina. But sidelong coition predisposes for rheumatic pains and sciatica.[78]

Manner the sixth – Make her get down on her knees and elbows, as if kneeling in prayer. In this position the vulva is projected backwards; you then attack her from that side, and put your member into her.[79]

Manner the seventh – Place the woman on her side, and squat between her thighs, with one of her legs on your shoulder and the other between your thighs, while she remains lying on her side. Then you enter her vagina, and make her move by drawing her towards your chest by means of your hands, with which you hold her embraced.

Manner the eighth – Let her stretch herself upon the ground, on her back, with her legs crossed; then mount her like a cavalier

[77] This position for coition, which may be called the natural one, is called by the Arabs *hannechi*, which means 'the manner of serpents.'

[78] The name of the side-coition is in Arabic *djenabi*, from *djeneb*, which means 'side, sidewards.'

[79] In vulgar Arabic, this manner of enjoying a woman is called *begouri*, that is to say, after the fashion of a bull.

on horseback, being on your knees, while her legs are placed
under her thighs, and put your member into her vagina.

Manner the ninth – Place the woman so that she leans with
her front, or, if you prefer it, her back upon a moderate elevation, with her feet set upon the ground. She thus offers her
vulva to the introduction of your member.[80]

Manner the tenth – Place the woman near to a low divan, the
back of which she can take hold of with her hands; then,
getting under her, lift her legs to the height of your navel, and
let her clasp you with her legs on each side of your body; in
this position plant your verge into her, seizing with your hands
the back of the divan. When you begin the action your movements must respond to those of the woman.

Manner the eleventh – Let her lie upon her back on the ground
with a cushion under her posterior; then getting between her
legs, and letting her place the sole of her right foot against the
sole of her left foot, introduce your member.

There are other positions besides the above named in use
among the peoples of India. It is well for you to know that the
inhabitants of those parts have multiplied the different ways to
enjoy women, and they have advanced farther than we in the
knowledge and investigation of coitus.

Amongst those manners are the following, called:

1. *El asemeud*, the stopperage.
2. *El modefedâ*, frog fashion.
3. *El mokefâ*, with the toes cramped.
4. *El mokeurmeutt*, with legs in the air.
5. *El setouri*, he-goat fashion.
6. *El loulabi*, the screw of Archimedes.
7. *El kelouci*, the summersault.

[80] Note in the autograph edition: It is necessary to observe that in all
these descriptions the couch where the encounter takes place is only an
Arabian bed, generally formed by several carpets laid one over the other,
or covering a mattress, which lies upon the ground. Such a bed is very
low, for which reason the author suggests an elevation (platform), when
the tryst requires a support of the height of our beds.

8. *Hachou en nekanok*, the tail of the ostrich.
9. *Lebeuss el djoureb*, fitting on of the sock.
10. *Kechef el astine*, reciprocal sight of the posteriors.
11. *Nezâ el kouss*, the rainbow arch.
12. *Nesedj el kheuzz*, alternative piercing.
13. *Dok el arz*, pounding on the spot.
14. *Nik el kohoul*, coition from the back.
15. *El keurchi*, belly to belly.
16. *El kebachi*, ram-fashion.
17. *Dok el outed*, driving the peg home.
18. *Sebek el heub*, love's fusion.
19. *Tred ech chate*, sheep-fashion.
20. *Kalen el miche*, interchange in coition.
21. *Rekeud el aïr*, the race of the member.
22. *El modakheli*, the fitter-in.
23. *El khouariki*, the one who stops in the house.
24. *Nik el haddadi*, the smith's coition.
25. *El moheundi*, the seducer.

FIRST MANNER – *El asemeud* (the stopperage). Place the woman on her back, with a cushion under her buttocks, then get between her legs, resting the points of your feet against the ground; bend her two thighs against her chest as far as you can; place your hands under her arms so as to enfold her or cramp her shoulders. Then introduce your member, and at the moment of ejaculation draw her towards you. This position is painful for the woman, for her thighs being bent upwards and her buttocks raised by the cushion, the walls of her vagina tighten, and the uterus tending forward there is not much room for movement, and scarcely space enough for the intruder; consequently the latter enters with difficulty and strikes against the uterus. This position should therefore not be adopted, unless the man's member is short or soft.

SECOND MANNER – *El modefedâ* (frog fashion). Place the woman on her back, and arrange her thighs so that they touch the heels, which latter are thus coming close to the buttocks; then down you sit in this kind of merry thought,[81] facing the vulva, in which you insert your member; you then place her knees under your arm-pits; and taking firm hold of the upper part of her arms, you draw her towards you at the crisis.

THIRD MANNER – *El mokefâ* (with the toes cramped). Place the woman on her back, and squat on your knees, between her thighs, gripping the ground with your toes; raise her knees as high as your sides, in order that she may cross her legs over your back, and then pass her arms round your neck.

FOURTH MANNER – *El mokeurmeutt* (with legs in the air). The woman lying on her back, you put her thighs together and raise her legs up until the soles of her feet look at the ceiling; then enfolding her within your thighs you insert your member, holding her legs up with your hands.

FIFTH MANNER – *El setouri* (he-goat fashion[82]). The woman being crouched on her side, you let her stretch out the leg on which she is resting, and squat down between her thighs with your calves bent under you;[83] then you lift her uppermost leg so that it rests on your back, and introduce your member. During the action you take hold of her shoulders, or, if you prefer it, by the arms.

SIXTH MANNER – *El loulabi* (the screw of Archimedes[84]). The man being stretched on his back the woman sits on his member, facing him; she then places her hands upon the bed so that she can keep her stomach from touching the man's, and

[81] The Arab text says *mokorfeuss*, which signifies the manner to squat on the ground with the arms slung round the legs. The root is a word of four letters, signifying: to tie somebody up by fastening his hands under his feet.

[82] The root of the word *setouri* is *seteur*, which means a he-goat.

[83] Note of the autograph edition. Here occurs the word *mokorfeuss*, mentioned in note 1, p. 75, and which has been translated with 'bending the calves.' This expression recurs frequently, preceded generally by the word *djeleuss*, 'to sit down.'

[84] The root of *el loulabi* is *louleb*, which means the pipe of a fountain, through which the water is forced, issuing out of a narrow opening, after a system which, like the screw of Archimedes, serves to raise water.

moves up and downwards, and if the man is supple he assists her from below. If in this position she wants to kiss him, she need only stretch her arms along the bed.

SEVENTH MANNER – *El kelouci* (the summersault). The woman must wear a pair of pantaloons, which she lets drop upon her heels; then she stoops, placing her head between her feet, so that her neck is in the opening of her pantaloons. At that moment the man, seizing her legs, turns her upon her back, making her perform a summersault; then with his legs curved under him he brings his member right against her vulva, and, slipping it between her legs, inserts it.

It is alleged that there are women who, while lying on their back, can place their feet behind their head without the help of pantaloons or hands.

EIGHTH MANNER – *Hachou en nekanok* (the tail of the ostrich). The woman lying on her back along the bed, the man kneels in front of her, lifting up her legs until her head and shoulders only are resting on the bed; his member having penetrated into her vagina, he seizes and sets into motion the buttocks of the woman who, on her part, twines her legs around his neck.[85]

NINTH MANNER – *Lebeuss el djoureb* (fitting on of the sock[86]). The woman lies on her back. You sit down between her legs and place your member between the lips of her vulva, which you fit over it with your thumb and first finger; then you move so as to procure for your member, as far as it is in contact with the woman, a lively rubbing, which action you continue until her vulva gets moistened with the liquid emitted from your verge. When she is thus amply prepared for enjoyment by the

---

[85] In taking notice of this position, it is easy to understand that the two legs of the woman raised up with the man's head between them may, to a certain extent, appear somewhat like an ostrich's tail.

[86] The author compares the virile member, which the man with the help of his hand envelopes, so to say, with the lips of the vulva before pushing it in, to the foot round which the Arab winds a piece of linen, called *djoureb*, previous to putting on his shoe.

alternate coming and going of your weapon in her scabbard, put it into her in full length.

TENTH MANNER – *Kechef el astine* (reciprocal sight of the posteriors[87]). The man lying stretched out on his back, the woman sits down upon his member with her back to the man's face, who presses her sides between his thighs and legs, whilst she places her hands upon the bed as a support for her movements, and lowering her head, her eyes are turned towards the buttocks of the man.[88]

ELEVENTH MANNER – *Nezâ el kouss* (the rainbow arch). The woman is lying on her side; the man also on his side, with his face towards her back, pushes in between her legs and introduces his member, with his hands lying on the upper part of her back. As to the woman, she then gets hold of the man's feet, which she lifts up as far as she can, drawing him close to her; thus she forms with the body of the man an arch, of which she is the rise.

TWELFTH MANNER – *Nesedj el kheuzz* (the alternate movement of piercing[89]). The man in sitting attitude places the soles of his feet together, and lowering his thighs, draws his feet nearer to his member; the woman sits down upon his feet, which he takes care to keep firm together. In this position the two thighs of the woman are pressed against the man's flanks, and she puts her arms round his neck. Then the man clasps the woman's ankles, and drawing his feet nearer to his body, brings the woman, who is sitting on them, within range of his member, which then enters her vagina. By moving his feet he sends her

---

[87] This posture has received the above name, because during the action each party can see the other's posterior. The name usually employed, *ras ou kaä*, literally signifying head and bottom, can be rendered in French *tête-bêche*.

[88] *Ast*, translated with justification, means the posterior; hence the word *setani*, meaning *paederast*.

[89] The word *nesedj* expresses the coming and going movement of the shuttle in weaving, the same being sent to and fro from one side to the other. The word *Kheuzz* means to perforate, to pierce through and through.

back and brings her forward again, without ever with-drawing his member entirely.

The woman makes herself as light as possible, and assists as well as she can in this come-and-go movement; her co-operation is, in fact, indispensable for it. If the man apprehends that his member may come out entirely, he takes her round the waist, and she receives no other impulse than that which is imparted to her by the feet of the man upon which she is sitting.

THIRTEENTH MANNER – *Dok el arz* (pounding on the spot[90]). The man sits down with his legs stretched out; the woman then places herself astride on his thighs, crossing her legs behind the back of the man, and places her vulva opposite his member, which latter she guides into her vagina; she then places her arms round his neck, and he embraces her sides and waist, and helps her to rise and descend upon his verge. She must assist in his work.

FOURTEENTH MANNER – *Nik el kohoul* (coitus from the back). The woman lies down on her stomach and raises her buttocks by help of a cushion; the man approaches from behind, stretches himself on her back and inserts his tool, while the woman twines her arms round the man's elbows. This is the easiest of all methods.

FIFTEENTH MANNER – *El keurchi* (belly to belly). The man and the woman are standing upright, face to face; she opens her thighs; the man then brings his feet forward between those of the woman, who also advances hers a little. In this position the man must have one of his feet somewhat in advance of the other. Each of the two has the arms round the other's hips; the man introduces his verge, and the two move thus intertwined after a manner called *neza' el dela*, which I shall explain later, if it please God the Almighty. (See FIRST MANNER.)

SIXTEENTH MANNER – *El kebachi* (after the fashion of the ram). The woman is on her knees, with her forearms on the ground; the man approaches from behind, kneels down, and lets

[90] The vulgar expression for this position is *nekahet el gada*, signifying coitus whilst sitting.

his member penetrate into her vagina, which she presses out as much as possible; he will do well in placing his hands on the woman's shoulders.

SEVENTEENTH MANNER – *Dok el outed* (driving the peg home). The woman enlaces with her legs the waist of the man, who is standing, with her arms passed round his neck, steadying herself by leaning against the wall. Whilst she is thus suspended the man insinuates his pin into her vulva.

EIGHTEENTH MANNER – *Sebek el heub* (love's fusion). While the woman is lying on her right side, extend yourself on your left side; your left leg remains extended, and you raise your right one till it is up to her flank, when you lay her upper leg upon your side. Thus her uppermost leg serves the woman as a support for her back. After having introduced your member you move as you please, and she responds to your action as she pleases.

NINETEENTH MANNER – *Tred ech chate* (coitus of the sheep[91]). The woman is on her hands and knees; the man, behind her, lifts her thighs till her vulva is on a level with his member, which he then inserts. In this position she ought to place her head between her arms.

TWENTIETH MANNER – *Kaleb el miche* (interchange in coition). The man lies on his back. The woman, gliding in between his legs, places herself upon him with her toe-nails against the ground; she lifts up the man's thighs, turning them against his own body, so that his virile member faces her vulva, into which she guides it; she then places her hands upon the bed by the sides of the man. It is, however, indispensable that the woman's feet rest upon a cushion to enable her to keep her vulva in concordance with his member.

In this position the parts are exchanged, the woman fulfilling that of the man, and vice-versa.

---

[91] The name *tred ech chate* – sheep's courtship – has received this name because the sheep, in receiving the caresses of the ram, puts its head between its legs, as is done by the woman in the position described.

There is a variation to this manner. The man stretches himself out upon his back, while the woman kneels with her legs under her, but between his legs. The remainder conforms exactly to what has been said above.

TWENTY-FIRST MANNER – *Rekeud el aïr* (the race of the member). The man, on his back, supports himself with a cushion under his shoulders, but his posterior must retain contact with the bed. Thus placed, he draws up his thighs until his knees are on a level with his face; then the woman sits down, impaling herself on his member; she must not lie down, but keep seated as if on horseback, the saddle being represented by the knees and the stomach of the man. In that position she can, by the play of her knees, work up and down and down and up. She can also place her knees on the bed, in which case the man accentuates the movement by plying his thighs, whilst she holds with her left hand on to his right shoulder.

TWENTY-SECOND MANNER – *El modakheli* (the fitter-in). The woman is seated on her coccyx, with only the points of her buttocks touching the ground; the man takes the same position, her vulva facing his member. Then the woman puts her right thigh over the left thigh of the man, whilst he on his part puts his right thigh over her left one.

The woman, seizing with her hands her partner's arms, gets his member into her vulva; and each of them leaning alternately a little back, and holding each other by the upper part of the arms, they initiate a swaying movement, moving with little concussions,[92] and keeping their movements in exact rhythm by the assistance of their heels, which are resting on the ground.

TWENTY-THIRD MANNER – *El khouariki* (the one who stops at home). The woman being couched on her back, the man lies down upon her, with cushions held in his hands.

After his member is in, the woman raises her buttocks as

[92] The author makes use of the word *nitah* derived from *netah*, and which is spoken of in note 12, p. 71.

high as she can off the bed, the man following her up with his member well inside; then the woman lowers herself again upon the bed, giving some short shocks, and although they do not embrace, the man must stick like glue to her. This movement they continue, but the man must make himself light and must not be ponderous, and the bed must be soft; in default of which the exercise cannot be kept up without break.

TWENTY-FOURTH MANNER – *Nik el haddadi* (the coition of the blacksmith). The woman lies on her back with a cushion under her buttocks, and her knees raised as far as possible towards her chest, so that her vulva stands out as a target; she then guides her partner's member in.

The man executes for some time the usual action of coition, then draws his tool out of the vulva, and glides it for a moment between the thighs of the woman, as the smith withdraws the glowing iron from the furnace in order to plunge it into cold water. This manner is called *sferdgeli*, position of the quince.

TWENTY-FIFTH MANNER – *El moheundi* (the seducer). The woman lying on her back, the man sits between her legs, with his croupe on his feet; then he raises and separates the woman's thighs, placing her legs under his arms, or over his shoulders; he then takes her round the waist, or seizes her shoulders.

The preceding descriptions furnish a large number of procedures, that cannot well be all put to the proof; but with such a variety to choose from, the man who finds one of them difficult to practice, can easily find plenty of others more to his convenience.

I have not made mention of positions which it appeared to me impossible to realize, and if there be anybody who thinks that those which I have described are not exhaustive, he has only to look for new ones.

It cannot be gainsaid that the Indians have surmounted the

greatest difficulties in respect to coition.[93] As a grand exploit, originating with them, the following may be cited:

> The woman being stretched out on her back, the man sits down on her chest, with his back turned to her face, his knees turned forward and his nails gripping the ground; he then raises her hips, arching her back until he has brought her vulva face to face with his member, which he then inserts, and thus gains his purpose.

This position, as you perceive, is very fatiguing and very difficult to attain. I even believe that the only realization of it consists in words and designs. With regard to the other methods described above, they can only be practised if both man and woman are free from physical defects, and of analogous construction; for instance, one or the other of them must not be humpbacked, or very little, or very tall, or too obese. And I repeat, that both must be in perfect health.

I shall now treat of coition between two persons of different conformation. I shall particularise the positions that will suit them in treating each of them severally.

I shall first discourse of the coition of a lean man and a corpulent woman, and the different postures they may assume for the act, assuming the woman to be lying down, and being turned successively over on her four sides.

If the man wants to work her sideways he takes the thigh of the woman which is uppermost, and raises it as high as possible on his flank, so that it rests over his waist; he employs her undermost arm as a pillow for the support of his head, and

---

[93] This is a reference by Nefzawi to the erotological manuals of ancient India. He probably had the Kama Sutra in mind, but might also have meant to indicate, among others: the *Ratirahasya* (Secrets of Love), the *Panchasakya* (Five Arrows), the *Smara Pradipa* (Light of Love), the *Rasmanjari* (Sprout of Love), and the *Ananga Ranga* (Stage of Love). Various paintings and examples of sculpture may also have been in his mind at the time, but this is mere surmise, for we cannot know whether or not he ever visited India. From his own text, however, one thing appears certain – he knew the contents of similar instructional works by learned Indians, for he mentions them more than once. (A.H.W.)

he takes care to place a stout cushion beneath his undermost hip, so as to elevate his member to the necessary height, which is indispensable on account of the thickness of the woman's thighs.

But if the woman has an enormous abdomen, projecting by reason of its obesity over her thighs and flanks, it will be best to lay her on her back, and to lift up her thighs towards her belly; the man kneels between them, having hold of her waist with his hands, and drawing her towards him; and if he cannot manage her in consequence of the obesity of her belly and thighs, he must with his two arms encircle her buttocks. But it is thus impossible for him to work her conveniently, owing to the want of mobility of her thighs, which are impeded by her belly. He may, however, support them with his hands, but let him take care not to place them over his own thighs, as, owing to their weight, he would not have the power nor the facility to move. As the poet has said:

> If you have to explore her, lift up her buttocks,
> In order to work like the rope thrown to a drowning man.
> You will then seem between her thighs
> Like a rower seated at the end of the boat.

The man can likewise couch the woman on her side, with the undermost leg in front; then he sits down on the thigh of that leg, his member being opposite her vulva, and lets her raise the upper leg, which she must bend at the knee. Then, with his hands seizing her legs and thighs, he introduces his member, with his body lying between her legs, his knees bent, and the points of his feet against the ground, so that he can elevate his posterior, and prevent her thighs from impeding the entrance. In this attitude they can enter into action.

If the woman's belly is enlarged by reason of her being with child, the man lets her lie down on one side; then placing one of her thighs over the other, he raises them both towards the stomach, without their touching the latter; he then lies down behind her on the same side, and can thus fit his member in. In this way he can thrust his tool in entirely, particularly by raising his foot, which is under the woman's leg, to the height of her thigh. The same may be done with a barren woman; but it is particularly to be recommended for the woman who is *enceinte*, as the above position offers the advantage of procuring her the pleasure she desires, without exposing her to any danger.

In the case of the man being obese, with a very pronounced rotundity of stomach, and the woman being thin, the best course to follow is to let the woman take the active part. To this end, the man lies down on his back with his thighs close together, and the woman lowers herself upon his member, astride of him; she rests her hands upon the bed, and he seizes her arms with his hands. If she knows how to move, she can thus, in turn, rise and sink upon his member; if she is not adroit enough for that movement, the man imparts a movement to her buttocks by the play of one of his thighs behind them. But if the man assumes this position, it may sometimes become prejudicial to him, inasmuch as some of the female sperm may penetrate into his urethra, and grave malady may ensue therefrom.[94] It may also happen – and that is just as bad – that the man's sperm cannot pass out, and returns into the urethra.

If the man prefers that the woman should lie on her back, he places himself, with his legs folded under him, between her legs, which she parts only moderately. Thus, his buttocks are between the woman's legs, with his heels touching them. In performing this way he will, however, feel fatigue, owing to the position of his stomach resting upon the woman's, and the inconvenience resulting therefrom; and, besides, he will not be able to get his whole member in the vulva.

It will be similar when both lie on their sides, as mentioned above in the case of pregnant women.

When both man and woman are fat, and wish to unite in

[94] This is a scientific error due to the beliefs of the period during which the work was written. See my remarks on the same subject in a footnote above, on page 129. (A.H.W.)

coition, they cannot contrive to do it without trouble, particularly when both have prominent stomachs. In these circumstances the best way to go about it is for the woman to be on her knees with her hands on the ground, so that her posterior is elevated; then the man separates her legs, leaving the points of the feet close together and the heels parted asunder; he then attacks her from behind, kneeling and holding up his stomach with his hand, and so introduces his member. Resting his stomach upon her buttocks during the act he holds the thighs or the waist of the woman with his hands. If her posterior is too low for his stomach to rest upon, he must place a cushion under her knees to remedy this.

I know of no other position so favourable as this for the coition of a fat man with a fat woman.

If, in fact, the man gets between the legs of a woman on her back under the above named circumstances, his stomach, encountering the woman's thighs, will not allow him to make free use of his tool. He cannot even see her vulva, or only in part; it may be almost said that it will be impossible for him to accomplish the act.

On the other hand, if the man makes the woman lie upon her side and then places himself, with his legs bent behind her, pressing his stomach upon the upper part of her posterior, she must draw her legs and thighs up to her stomach, in order to lay bare her vagina and allow the introduction of his member; but if she cannot sufficiently bend her knees, the man can neither see her vulva, nor explore it.

If, however, the stomach of each person is not exaggeratedly large, they can manage very well all positions. Only they must not be too long in coming to the crisis, as they will soon feel fatigued and lose their breath.

In the case of a very big man and a very little woman, the difficulty to be solved is how to contrive that their organs of generation and their mouths can meet at the same time. To gain this end the woman had best lie on her back; the man places himself on his side near her, passes one of his hands under her neck, and with the other raises her thighs till he can put his member against her vulva from behind, the woman remaining still on her back. In this position he holds her up with his hands by the neck and the thighs. He can then enter her body, while the woman on her part puts her arms round his neck, and approaches her lips to his.

If the man wishes the woman to lie on her side, he gets between her legs, and, placing her thighs so that they are in contact with his sides, one above and one under, he glides in between them till his member is facing her vulva from behind; he then presses his thighs against her buttocks, which he seizes with one hand in order to impart movement to them; the other hand he has round her neck. If the man then likes, he can get his thighs over those of the woman, and press her towards him; this will make it easier for him to move.

As regards the copulation of a very small man and a tall woman, the two actors cannot kiss each other while in action unless they take one of the three following positions, and even then they will become fatigued.

FIRST POSITION – The woman lies on her back, with a thick cushion under her buttocks, and a similar one under her head; she then draws up her thighs as far as possible towards her chest. The man lies down upon her, introduces his member, and takes hold of her shoulders, drawing himself up towards them. The woman winds her arms and legs round his back, whilst he holds on to her shoulders, or, if he can, to her neck.

SECOND POSITION – Man and woman lie both on their side, face to face; the woman slips her undermost thigh under the man's flank, drawing it at the same time higher up; she does the like with her other thigh over his; then she arches her stomach out, while his member is penetrating into her. Both should have hold of the other's neck, and the woman, crossing her legs over his back, should draw the man towards her.

THIRD POSITION – The man lies on his back, with his legs stretched out; the woman sits on his member, and, stretching herself down over him, draws up her knees to the height of her stomach; then, laying her hands over his shoulders, she draws herself up, and presses her lips to his.

All these postures are more or less fatiguing for both; people can, however, choose any other position they like; but they must be able to kiss each other during the act.

I will now speak to you of those who are little, in consequence of being humpbacked. Of these there are several kinds.

First, there is the man who is crookbacked, but whose spine and neck are straight. For him it is most convenient to unite himself with a little woman, but not otherwise than from behind. Placing himself behind her posterior, he thus introduces his member into her vulva. But if the woman is in a stooping attitude, on her hands and feet, he will do still better. If the woman be afflicted with a hump and the man is straight, the same position is suitable.

If both of them are crookbacked they can take what position they like for coition. They cannot, however, embrace; and if they lie on their side, face to face, there will be left an empty space between them. And if one or the other lies down on the back, a cushion must be placed under the head and the shoulder, to hold them up, and fill the place which is left vacant.

In the case of a man whose malformation affects only his neck, so as to press his chin towards his chest, but who is otherwise straight, he can take any position he likes for doing the business, and give himself up to any embraces and caresses, always excepting kisses on the mouth. If the woman is lying on her back, he will appear in action as if he were butting at her like a ram. If the woman has her neck deformed in similar manner, their coition will resemble the mutual attack of two horned beasts with their heads. The most convenient position for them will be that the woman should stoop down, and he

K

attack her from behind. The man whose hump appears on his back in the shape of only the half of a jar is not so much disfigured as the one of whom the poet has said:

> Lying on his back he is a dish;
> Turn him over, and you have a dish-cover.

In his case coition can take place as with any other man who is small in stature and straight; he cannot, however, easily lie on his back.

If a little woman is lying on her back, with a humpbacked man upon her belly, he will look like the cover over a vase. If, on the contrary, the woman is large-sized, he will have the appearance of a carpenter's plane in action. I have made the following verses on this subject:

> The humpback is vaulted like an arch;
> And seeing him you cry, 'Glory be to God!'
> You ask him how he manages in coitus?
> 'It is the retribution for my sins,' he says.
> The woman under him is like a board of deal;
> The humpback, who explores her, does the planing.

I have also said in verse:

> The humpback's dorsal cord is tied in knots,
> The Angels tire with writing all his sins;[95]
> In trying for a wife of proper shape;
> And for her favours, she repulses him,
> And says, 'Who bears the wrongs we shall commit?'
> And he, 'I bear them well upon my hump!'
> And then she mocks him saying, 'Oh, you plane
> Destined for making shavings! take a deal board!'

If the woman has a hump as well as the man, they may take any of the various positions for coition, always observing that if one of them lies on the back, the hump must be environed with cushion, as with a turban, thus having a nest to lie in, which guards its top, which is very tender. In this way they can embrace closely.

[95] Note in the autograph edition. The angels, according to the creed of the Mussulmans, are incessantly busy in writing down, whilst standing behind or before a man, his good and bad actions. (See the *Koran*, chap. vi, verse 61, and chap. xiii, verse 12.)

If the man is humped both on back and chest he must re-
nounce the embrace and the clinging, but can otherwise take
any position he likes for coition. Yet generally speaking, the
action must always be troublesome for himself and the woman.
I have written on this subject :

> The humpback engaged in the act of coition
> Is like a vase provided with two handles.
> If he is burning for a woman, she will tell him,
> 'Your hump is in the way; you cannot do it;
> Your verge would find a place to rummage in,
> But on your chest the hump, where would it be?'

If both the woman and the man have double humps, the
best position they can assume for coitus is the following : 'Whilst
the woman is lying on her side, the man introduces his member
after the fashion described previously in respect to pregnant
women. Thus the two humps do not encounter one another.
Both are lying on their sides, and the man attacks from behind.
Should the woman be on her back, her hump must be supported
by a cushion, whilst the man kneels between her legs, she holding up her posterior. Thus placed, their two humps are not
near each other, and all inconvenience is avoided.

The same is the case if the woman stoops down with her
head, with her croup in the air, after the manner of *El kouri*,
which position will suit both of them, if they have the chest
malformed, but not the back. One of them then performs the
action of come-and-go.

But the most curious and amusing description which I have
ever met in this respect, is contained in these verses :

> Their two extremities are close together,
> And nature made a laughing stock of them;
> Foreshortened he appears as if cut off;
> He looks like someone bending to escape a blow,
> Or like a man who has received a blow
> And shrivels down so as to miss a second.

If a man's spine is curved about the hips and his back is
straight, so that he looks as though he was in prayer, half

prostrated, coition for him is very difficult; owing to the reciprocal positions of his thighs and his stomach, he cannot possibly insert his member entirely, as it lies so far back between his thighs. The best for him to do is to stand up. The woman stoops down before him with her hands to the ground, and her posterior in the air; he can thus introduce his member as a pivot for the woman to move upon, for, be it observed, he cannot well move himself. It is the manner El *kouri*, with the difference, that it is the woman who moves.

A man may be attacked by the illness called *ikaad*, or *zomana* (paralysis), which compels him to be constantly seated. If this malady only affects his knees and legs, his thighs and spinal column remaining sound, he can use all the sundry positions for coition, except those where he would have to stand up. In the case of his buttocks being affected, even if he is otherwise perfectly well, it is the woman who will have to make all the movements.

Know that the most enjoyable coitus does not always exist in the manners described here; I only give them, so as to render this work as complete as possible. Sometimes most enjoyable coition takes place between lovers, who, not quite perfect in their proportions, find their own means for their mutual gratification.[96]

It is said that there are women of great experience who, lying with a man, elevate one of their feet vertically in the air, and upon that foot a lamp is set full of oil, and with the wick burning. While the man is ramming them, they keep the lamp steady and burning, and the oil is not spilled. Their coition is in no way impeded by this exhibition, but it must require great previous practice on the part of both.

[96] A very wise piece of observation which might well be turned into good advice. In fact it should be said here that in love-making, as in everything else, it is a mistake to follow a book of rules too closely. The rules, the ways, the manners, should certainly be learnt and studied – but Love herself, and nature seconded by mutual respect, must be the ultimate masters. (A.H.W.)

Assuredly the Indian writers have in their works described a great many ways of making love, but the majority of them do not yield enjoyment, and give more pain than pleasure. That which is to be looked for in coition, the crowning point of it, is the enjoyment, the embrace, the kisses. This is the distinction between the coitus of men and that of animals. No one is indifferent to the enjoyment which proceeds from the difference between the sexes, and man finds his highest felicity in it.

If the desire of love in man is roused to its highest pitch, all the pleasures of coition become easy for him, and he satisfies his yearning in any way.

It is well for the lover of coition to put all these manners to the proof, so as to ascertain which is the position that gives the greatest pleasure to both combatants. Then he will know which to choose for the tryst, and in satisfying his desires retain the woman's affection.

Many people have essayed all the positions I have described, but none has been as much approved of as the *Dok el arz*.

A story is told on this subject of a man who had a wife of incomparable beauty, graceful and accomplished. He used to explore her in the ordinary manner, never having recourse to any other. The woman experienced none of the pleasure which ought to accompany the act, and was consequently generally very moody after the coition was over.

The man complained about this to an old dame, who told him, 'Try different ways in uniting yourself to her, until you find the one which best satisfies her. Then work her in this fashion only, and her affection for you will know no limit.'

He then tried upon his wife various manners of coition, and when he came to the one called *Dok el arz* he saw her overcome by violent transports of love, and at the crisis of pleasure he felt her womb grasp his verge energetically; and she said to him, biting his lips, 'This is the veritable manner of making love!'

These demonstrations proved to the lover, in fact, that his

mistress felt in that position the most lively pleasure, and he always thenceforward worked with her in that way. Thus he attained his end, and caused the woman to love him to folly.

Therefore try different manners; for every woman likes one in preference to all other for her pleasure. The majority of them have, however, a predilection for the *Dok el arz*, as, in the application of the same, belly is pressed to belly, mouth glued to mouth, and the action of the womb is rarely absent.

I have now only to mention the various movements practised during coitus, and shall describe some of them.

FIRST MOVEMENT – *Neza el dela* (the bucket in the well). The man and woman join in close embrace after the introduction. Then he gives a push, and with-draws a little; the woman follows him with a push, and also retires. So they continue their alternate movement, keeping proper time. Placing foot against foot, and hand against hand, they keep up the motion of a bucket in a well.

SECOND MOVEMENT – *El netahi* (the mutual shock). After the introduction, they each draw back, but without dislodging the member completely. Then they both push tightly together, and thus go on keeping time.

THIRD MOVEMENT – *El motadani* (the approach). The man moves as usual, and then stops. Then the woman, with the member in her receptacle, begins to move like the man, and then stops. And they continue this way until the ejaculation comes.

FOURTH MOVEMENT – *Khiate el heub* (Love's tailor). The man, with his member being only partially inserted in the vulva, keeps up a sort of quick friction with the part that is in, and then suddenly plunges his whole member in up to its root. This is the movement of the needle in the hands of the tailor, of which the man and woman must take cognisance.

Such a movement only suits those men and women who can at will retard the crisis. With those who are otherwise constituted it would act too quickly.

FIFTH MOVEMENT – *Souak el feurdj* (the toothpick in the vulva). The man introduces his member between the walls of the vulva, and then drives it up and down, and right and left. Only a man with a very vigorous member can execute this movement.

SIXTH MOVEMENT – *Tâchik el heub* (the boxing up of love). The man introduces his member entirely into the vagina, so closely that his hairs are completely mixed up with the woman's. In that position he must now move forcibly, without with-drawing his tool in the least.

This is the best of all the movements, and is particularly well adapted to the position *Dok el arz*. Women prefer it to any other kind, as it procures them the extreme pleasure of seizing the member with their womb; and appeases their lust most completely.

Those women called *tribades* always use this movement in their mutual caresses. And it provokes prompt ejaculation both with man and woman.

Without kissing, no kind of position or movement procures the fullest pleasure; and those positions in which the kiss is not practicable are not entirely satisfactory, considering that the kiss is one of the most powerful stimulants to the work of love.[97]

I have said in verse:

> The languishing eye
> Puts in connection soul with soul,
> And the tender kiss
> Takes the message from member to vulva.

The kiss is assumed to be an integral part of coition. The best kiss is the one impressed on humid lips combined with the suction of the lips and tongue, which latter particularly pro-

[97] This is all very true. A little known European saying is that 'A kiss is the most potent of aphrodisiacs'; Havelock Ellis and others have pointed out the importance of the kiss in love-play (as well as during and after the act), and its function in promoting and maintaining tumescence. (A.H.W.)

vokes the flow of sweet and fresh saliva. It is for the man to bring this about by slightly and softly nibbling his partner's tongue, when her saliva will flow sweet and exquisite, more pleasant than refined honey, and which will not mix with the saliva of her mouth. This manoeuvre will give the man a trembling sensation, which will run all through his body, and is more intoxicating than wine drunk to excess.

A poet has said:

> In kissing her, I have drunk from her mouth
> Like a camel that drinks from the *redir*;[98]
> Her embrace and the freshness of her mouth
> Give me a languor that goes to my marrow.

The kiss should be sonorous; it originates with the tongue touching the palate, lubricated by saliva. It is produced by the movement of the tongue in the mouth and by the displacement of the saliva, provoked by the suction.

The kiss given to the superficial outer part of the lips, and making a noise comparable to the one by which you call your cat, gives no pleasure. It is well enough thus applied to children and hands.

The kiss I have described above is the one for coitus and is full of voluptuousness.

A vulgar proverb says:

> A humid kiss
> Is better than a hurried coitus.[99]

I have composed on this subject the following lines:

> You kiss my hand – my mouth should be the place!
> O woman, thou who art my idol!
> It was a fond kiss you gave me, but it is lost,
> The hand cannot appreciate the nature of a kiss.

---

[98] Note of the autograph edition: The *redir* is a natural reservoir in the hot plains, in which the rainwater collects. It is a precious hoard for nomadic populations.

[99] This proverb has often been repeated through the ages, and might be taken as sound advice by many of our contemporary devotees of 'rush, speed, and impatience'. (A.H.W.)

The three words, *Kobla*, *letsem*, and *bouss*[100] are used indiffer-
ently to indicate the kiss on the hand or on the mouth. The
word *ferame* means specially the kiss on the mouth.

An Arab poet has said:

> The heart of love can find no remedy
> In witching sorcery nor amulets,
> Nor in the fond embrace without a kiss,
> Nor in a kiss without coitus.

And the author of the work, 'The Jewels of the Bride and the
Rejoicing of Souls,' has added to the above, as complement and
commentary, the two following verses:

> Nor in converse, however unrestrained,
> But in the placing of legs on legs (coition).

Remember that all caresses and all sorts of kisses, as described,
are of no account without the introduction of the member.
Therefore abstain from them, if you do not want action; they
only fan a fire to no purpose.[101] The passion which is excited
resembles in fact a fire which is being lighted; and just as water
only can extinguish the latter, so only the emission of the sperm
can calm the lust and appease the heat.

The woman is not more advantaged than the man by caresses
without coition.

It is said that Dahama bent Mesedjel appeared before the
Governor of the province of Yamama, with her father and her

---

[100] The Arabic word *bouss*, indicating a specific kind of kiss, seems similar to an old English word frequently employed by Burton in his translation of the *Arabian Nights*: buss (i.e. 'They toyed and bussed one another
in pleasant dalliance'). 'Buss', which means literally 'kiss', is probably
derived from the French 'baiser' (Latin: *basiare*, *basium*). Note also the
title of some of the love poems of Johannes Secundus: *Bassia* (Kisses).
(A.H.W.)

[101] This is only commonsense, and is sound advice to the young, who
frequently do not realise the potency of the kiss in arousing erotic desire.
The warning is especially applicable to young girls, who never seem to
appreciate the danger (and the invitation) implicit in a kiss. Young
men, of course, owing to their more immediate physiological response,
are not so innocent of the fire inherent in a kiss. An old French proverb,
rendered somewhat more politely than in its original form, runs: 'When
a woman kisses she desires coition....' (A.H.W.)

husband, El Adjadje, alleging that the latter was impotent, and did not cohabit with her nor come near her.

Her father, who assisted her in her case, was reproached for mixing himself up with her plaint by the people of Yamama, who said to him, 'Are you not ashamed to help your daughter in bringing a claim for coition?'

To which he answered, 'It is my wish that she should have children; if she loses them it will be by God's will; if she brings them up they will be useful to her.'

Dahama formulated her claim thus in coming before the Governor: 'There stands my husband, and until now he has never touched me.' The Governor interposed, saying, 'No doubt this is because you have been unwilling?' 'On the contrary,' she replied, 'it is for him that I open my thighs and lie down on my back.' Then cried the husband, 'O Emir, she tells untruth; in order to possess her I have to fight with her.' The Emir pronounced the following judgment: 'I give you,' he said, 'a year's time to prove her allegation to be false.' He decided thus out of regard for the man. El Adjadje then went away reciting those verses:

> Dahama and her father Mesedjel thought
> The Emir would decide upon my impotence.
> Is not the stallion sometimes lazy-minded?
> And yet he is so large and vigorous.

Returned to his house he began to kiss and caress his wife; but his efforts went no farther, he remained incapable of giving proofs of his virility. Dahama said to him, 'Keep your caresses and embraces; they do not satisfy love. What I desire is a solid and stiff member, the sperm of which will flow into my matrix.' And she recited to him the following verses:

> Before God! it is in vain to try with kisses
> To entertain me, and with your embracings!
> To still my torments I must feel a member,
> Ejaculating sperm into my uterus.

El Adjadje, in despair, conducted her forthwith back to her family, and, to hide his shame, repudiated her that very night.

A poet said on that occasion:

> What are caresses to an ardent woman,
> Or costly vestments and fine jewellery,[102]
> If the man's organs do not meet her own,
> And she is yearning for the virile verge?

Know then that the majority of women do not find full satisfaction in kisses and embraces without coition. For them satisfaction resides only in the member, and they like the man who rummages them, even if he is ugly and misshapen.

A story also goes on this subject that Moussa ben Mesâb betook himself one day to a woman in the town who had a female slave, an excellent singer, whom he wanted to buy from her. This woman was resplendently beautiful, and independent of her charming appearance, she had a large fortune. He saw at the same time in the house a young man of bad shape and ungainly appearance, who went to and fro giving orders.

Moussa having asked who the man was, she told him, 'This is my husband, and for him I would give my life!' 'This is a hard slavery,' he said, 'to which you are reduced, and I am sorry for you. We belong to God, and shall return to him![103] but what a misfortune it is that such incomparable beauty and such delightful forms as I see in you should be for such a man!'

She made answer, 'O son of my mother,[104] if he could do to you from behind what he does for me in front, you would sell your lately acquired fortune as well as your patrimony. He would appear to you beautiful, and his plain looks would be changed into beauty.'

'May God preserve him to you!'[105] said Moussa.

---

[102] Note of the autograph edition: The author cites here two names of costly garments: *l'ouchahane* and the *djelbab*. For the translation it appeared better not to cling to the latter, but to give the true sense, which is: 'luxurious garments and jewellery.'

[103] Note of the autograph edition: The Mussulman formula expressing resignation. (See Koran, chap. ii, verse 151.)

[104] Id. A familiar expression, not exactly implying that he who is thus addressed is the brother of the person who uses it.

[105] Id. Literally, 'God bless you in this respect.'

It is also said that the poet Farazdak met one day a woman on whom he cast a glance burning with love, and who for that reason thus addressed him: 'What makes you look at me in this fashion? Had I a thousand vulvas, there would be nothing to hope for you!' 'And why?' said the poet. 'Because your appearance is not prepossessing,' she said, 'and what you keep hidden will be no better.' He replied, 'If you would put me to the proof, you would find that my interior qualities are of a nature to make you forget my outer appearance.' He then uncovered himself, and let her see a member the size of the arm of a young girl. At that sight she felt herself burning hot with amorous desire. He saw this, and asked her to let him caress her. Then she uncovered herself and showed him her mount of Venus, vaulted like a cupola.[106] He then did the business for her, and recited these verses:

> I have plied in her my member, big as a virgin's arm;
> A member with a round head, and prompt to attack;
> Measuring in length a span and a half,
> And, oh! I felt as though I had put it in a brazier.

He who seeks the pleasure a woman can give must satisfy her amorous desire for hot caresses, as described. He will see her swooning with lust, her vulva will get moist, her womb will stretch forward, and the two sperms will come together.

[106] Note of the autograph edition: Here appears the taste of the Arabs for a prominent pubis. The subject of this structural quality of women will appear frequently.

CHAPTER VII

Of Matters which are Injurious in the Act of Generation

K NOW, O VIZIR (to whom God be good!), that the ills caused by coition are numerous. I will mention to you some of them, which to know is essential, in order to be able to avoid them.

Let me tell you in the first place that coition, if performed standing, affects the knee-joints and brings about nervous shiverings; and if performed sideways will predispose your system for gout and sciatica, which resides chiefly in the hip joint.

Do not mount upon a woman fasting or immediately before making a meal, or else you will have pains in your back, you will lose your vigour, and your eyesight will get weaker.

If you do it with the woman bestriding you, your dorsal cord will suffer and your heart will be affected; and if in that position the smallest drop of the usual secretions of the vagina enters your urethral canal, a painful stricture may supervene.

Do not leave your member in the vulva after ejaculation, as this might cause gravel, or softening of the vertebral column, or the rupture of blood vessels, or lastly, inflammation of the lungs.[107]

---

[107] Once more this is nonsense, due to the superstition of the times. It scarcely seems necessary to point out these errors in the light of our modern knowledge. In so far as the history of medicine is concerned, however, such beliefs are not without interest. (A.H.W).

Too much exercise after coition is also detrimental.

Avoid washing your member after the copulation, as this may cause canker.

As to coition with old women, it acts like a fatal poison, and it has been said, 'Do not rummage old women, were they as rich as Karoun.'[108] And it has further been said, 'Beware of mounting old women; and if they cover you with favours.' And again, 'The coitus of old women is a venomous meal.'

Know that the man who works a woman younger than he is himself acquires new vigour; if she is of the same age as he is he will derive no advantage from it; and, finally, if it is a woman older than himself she will take all his strength out of him for herself. The following verses treat on this subject:

> Be on your guard and shun coition with old women;
> In her bosom she bears the poison of the *arakime*.[109]

A proverb says also, 'Do not serve an old woman, even if she offered to feed you with semolina and almond bread.'

The excessive practice of coition injures the health on account of the expenditure of too much sperm. For as butter made of cream represents the quintessence of the milk, and if you take the cream off, the milk loses its qualities, even so does the sperm form the quintessence of nutrition, and its loss is debilitating. On the other hand, the condition of the body, and consequently the quality of the sperm depends directly upon the food you take. If, therefore, a man will passionately give himself up to the enjoyment of coition, without undergoing too great fatigue, he must live upon strengthening food, exciting comfits,[110] aromatic plants, meat, honey, eggs, and other similar

---

[108] This Karoun, the Cora of the Bible, is reported by the expositors to have constructed a palace all covered with gold, the doors being of solid gold. He generally rode a white mule covered with golden trappings.

[109] Note of the autograph edition: Arakime is the plural of Arkeum, the name of a hideous serpent whose sting is fatal.

[110] These comfits are called *madjoun*, and are prepared from fruit, particularly from cherries and pears cooked with honey. According as they may be wanted more or less spiced, there are added, in varying quantities, cinnamon, musk, etc.

viands. He who follows such a régime is protected against the following accidents, to which excessive coition may lead.

Firstly, the loss of generative power.

Secondly, the deterioration of his sight; for although he may not become blind, he will at least have to suffer from eye diseases if he does not follow my advice.

Thirdly, the loss of his physical strength; he may become like the man who wants to fly but cannot, who pursuing somebody cannot catch him, or who carrying a burden, or working, soon gets tired and prostrated.

He who does not want to feel the necessity for coition uses camphor. Half of a *mitskal*[111] of this substance, macerated in water, makes the man who drinks of it insensible to the pleasures of copulation. Many women use this remedy when in fits of jealousy against rivals,[112] or when they need repose after great excesses. Then they try to procure camphor that has been left after a burial, and shrink from no expense of money to get such from the old women who have the charge of the corpses.[113] They also make use of the flower of henna, which is called *faria*;[114] they macerate the same in water, until it turns yellow, and thus supply themselves with a beverage which has almost the same effect as camphor.

I have treated of these remedies in the present chapter, although this is not their proper place; but I thought that this information, as here given, may be of use to many persons.

There are certain things which will become injurious if constantly indulged in and which in the end affect the health. Such

[111] The *mitskal* is a weight of 3/7th of a *dirhem*, corresponding to a drachm and a half of our old system of weights, and is therefore equal to one gramme and ninety centigrammes.

[112] The word *deraïr* – the singular number of which is *derra*, and which is rendered in the translation with rivals – comes from a root which signifies to be injurious.

[113] With the Mussulmans it is customary to wash the dead, with the greatest assiduity, with perfumed waters before they are buried.

[114] Henna is a plant which is in great demand with Arabs. The dried leaves of it are reduced to a powder or steeped in water, and are then used to rouge the nails, feet, hands, hair and beard.

are: too much sleep, long voyages in unfavourable season, which latter, particularly in cold countries, may weaken the body and cause disease of the spine. The same effects may arise from the habitual handling of those bodies which engender cold and humidity, like plaster, etc.

For people who have difficulty in passing water coitus is hurtful.

The habit of consuming acid food is debilitating.

To keep one's member in the vulva of a woman after ejaculation has taken place, be it for a long or a short time, enfeebles that organ and makes it less fit for coition.

If you are lying with a woman, do her business several times if you feel inclined, but take care not to overdo it, for it is a true word that 'He who plays the game of love for his own sake, and to satisfy his desires, feels the most intense and durable pleasure; but he who does it to satisfy the lust of another person will languish, lose all his desire, and finish by becoming impotent for coition.'

The sense of these words is, that a man when he feels disposed for it can give himself up to the exercise of coitus with more or less ardour according to his desires, and at the time which best suits him, without any fear of future impotence, if his enjoyment is provoked and regulated only by his feeling the want of lying with a woman.

But he who makes love for the sake of somebody else, that is to say only to satisfy the passion of his mistress, and tries all he can to attain that impossibility, that man will act against his own interest and imperil his health to please another person.

As injurious may be considered coition in the bath or immediately after leaving the bath; after having been bled or purged or such like. Coitus after a heavy bout of drinking is likewise to be avoided. To indulge coitus with a woman during her courses is as detrimental to the man as to the woman herself, as at that time her blood is vitiated and her womb cold, and if the least drop of blood should get in the man's urinary canal numerous maladies may supervene. As to the woman, she feels no pleasure during her courses, and at such time holds coitus in aversion.

As regards copulation in the bath, some say that there is no pleasure to be derived from it, if, as is believed, the degree of enjoyment is dependent upon the warmth of the vulva; for in the bath the vulva cannot be otherwise than cold, and consequently unfit for giving pleasure. And it is besides not to be forgotten that the water penetrating into the sexual parts of man or woman may lead to grave consequences.

Coitus after a full meal may occasion rupture of the intestines.[115] It is also to be avoided after undergoing much fatigue, or at a time of very hot or very cold weather.

Amongst the accidents which may attend the act of coition in hot countries may be mentioned sudden blindness without any previous symptoms.

The repetition of the coitus without washing the parts ought to be shunned, as it may enfeeble the virile power.

The man must also abstain from copulation with his wife if he is in a state of legal impurity,[116] for if she should become pregnant by such coition the child could not be sound.

After ejaculation do not remain close to the woman, as the disposition for recommencing will suffer by doing so.

[115] Coitus after a full meal is never to be recommended, especially in the middle-aged, or older. But in the absence of an appropriate disease it is certainly not at all likely to cause 'rupture of the intestines'. Death from heart-failure in certain specifically predisposed persons (one is almost inclined to say 'patients') is, nevertheless, not an impossibility; and cardiac patients should certainly consult their medical adviser regarding the amount of, and conditions for coitus. (A.H.W.)

[116] Note in the autographic edition : Legal impurity is due to different causes, enumerated by Sidi Khelil, in chap. i of his *Religious Jurisprudence*. The same disappears by ablution or by lotion. To give an example, I shall cite the following extract from that chapter. 'The lotion is obligatory for any male person arrived at the age of puberty who has introduced *only* the gland of his verge, be it in carnal connection with a woman, or with an animal, or with a corpse, or (in case of malformation, or on account of flaccidity) who has thus introduced part of his verge to the length of the gland.' (Translation of Perron.)

L

Care is to be taken not to carry heavy loads on one's back or to over-exert the mind, if one does not want the coitus to be impeded. It is also not good constantly to wear vestments made of silk,[117] as they impair all the energy for copulation. Silken cloths worn by women also affect injuriously the capacity for erection of the virile member.

Fasting, if prolonged, calms sexual desire; but in the beginning it excites the same.

Abstain from greasy liquids, as in the course of time they diminish the strength necessary for coition.

The effect of snuff, whether plain or scented, is similar.[118]

It is bad to wash the sexual parts with cold water directly after copulation; in general, washing with cold water calms down the desire, while warm water strengthens it.

Conversation with a young woman excites in a man the erection and passion commensurate with the youthfulness of the woman.

An Arab addressed the following recommendation to his daughter at the time when he conducted her to her husband: 'Perfume yourself with water!' meaning that she should frequently wash her body with water in preference to perfumes; the latter, moreover, not being suitable for everyone.

It is also reported that a woman having said to her husband, 'You are then a nobody, as you never perfume yourself!' he

[117] It is probably owing to the great warmth developed by silk that the author thinks the wearing of silken stuffs to be injurious with respect to coition. It may, in fact, be admitted that they have that effect.
[118] Tobacco has always been regarded as an anaphrodisiac, and the same deterrent effects have been attributed to snuff. Years ago the Goncourt brothers (*Journal des Goncourts*) said: 'There is an antagonism between tobacco and women. The taste for one diminishes the taste for the other. So true is this that passionate Lotharios usually give up smoking, because they feel . . . that tobacco diminishes their sexual appetite and . . . powers.' For some other references see *Aphrodisiacs: From Legend to Prescription*, by Alan Hull Walton, Connecticut, 1958, pages 47, 93, 128, 193-4 (originally published in a limited edition by Charles Skilton, London, 1956 – the pagination is identical in both editions, but the American volume has an additional Introductic⁻ ʰᵛ Herman Goodman, M.D., of New York). (A.H.W.)

made answer, 'Oh, you sloven! it is for the woman to emit a sweet odour.'

The abuse of coition is followed by loss of the taste for its pleasures; and to remedy this loss the sufferer must anoint his member with a mixture of the blood of a he-goat with honey. This will procure for him a marvellous effect in making love.

It is said that reading the Koran also predisposes for copulation.

Remember that a prudent man will beware of abusing the enjoyment of coition. The sperm is the water of life; if you use it economically you will always be ready for love's pleasures; it is the light of your eye; do not be lavish with it at all times and whenever you have a fancy for enjoyment, for if you are not sparing with it you will expose yourself to many ills. Wise medical men say, 'A robust constitution is indispensable for copulation, and he who is endowed with it may give himself up to the pleasure without danger; but it is otherwise with the weakly man; he runs into danger by indulging freely with women.'

The sage, Es Sakli, has thus determined the limits to be observed by man as to the indulgence of the pleasures of coition: Man, be he phlegmatic or sanguine, should not make love more than twice or thrice a month; bilious or hypochondriac men only once or twice a month. It is nevertheless a well established fact that nowadays men of any of these four temperaments are insatiable as to coition, and give themselves up to it day and night, taking no heed how they expose themselves to numerous ills, both internal and external.

Women are more favoured than men in indulging their passion for coition. It is in fact their specialty; and for them it is all pleasure; while men run many risks in abandoning themselves without reserve to the pleasures of love.

Having thus treated of the dangers which may occur from the coitus, I have considered it useful to bring to your knowledge the following verses, which contain hygienic advice in their respect. These verses have been composed by the order of Haroun er Rachid[119] by the most celebrated physicians of his time, whom he had asked to inform him of the remedies for successfully combating the ills caused by coition.

> Eat slowly, if your food shall do you good,
> And take good care, that it be well digested.
> Beware of things which want hard mastication;
> They are bad nourishment, so keep from them.
> Drink not directly after finishing your meal,
> Or else you go half way to meet an illness.
> Keep not within you what is of excess,
> And if you were in most susceptible circles,
> Attend to this well before seeking your bed,
> For rest this is the first necessity.
> From medicines and drugs keep well away,
> And do not use them unless very ill.
> Use all precautions proper, for they keep
> Your body sound, and are the best support.
> Don't be too eager for round-breasted women;
> Excess of pleasure soon will make you feeble,
> And in coition you may find a sickness;
> And then you find too late that in coition
> Our spring of life runs into woman's vulva.
> And before all beware of aged women,
> For their embraces will to you be poison.
> Each second day a bath should wash you clean;
> Remember these precepts and follow them.

Those were the rules given by the sages to the master of benevolence and goodness, to the generous of the generous.

All sages and physicians agree in saying that the ills which afflict man originate with the abuse of coition. The man therefore who wishes to preserve his health, and particularly his sight, and who wants to lead a pleasant life, will indulge with moderation in love's pleasures, aware that the greatest evils may spring therefrom.

[119] The Haroun er Rachid in question was Kalif in the year 170, and was acknowledged to have been one of the most meritorious, eloquent, cultured and generous of rulers.

CHAPTER VIII

The Sundry Names given to the Sexual Parts of Man

K NOW, O VIZIR (to whom God be good!), that man's
member bears different names, as: [120]

El *de keur*, the virile member.
El *kamera*, the penis.
El *aïr*, the member for generation.
El *hamama*, the pigeon.
El *teunnana*, the tinkler.
El *heurmak*, the indomitable.
El *ahlil*, the liberator.
El *zeub*, the verge.
El *hammache*, the exciter.
El *nâasse*, the sleeper.
El *zodamme*, the crowbar.
El *khiade*, the tailor.
Mochefi *el relil*, the extinguisher of passion.
El *khorrate*, the turnabout.
El *deukkak*, the striker.
El *âouame*, the swimmer.

[120] Rabelais also gives in his history of Pantagruel divers more or less
curious names to the organ of generation of man.

El *dekhal*, the housebreaker.

El *âouar*, the one-eyed.

El *fortass*, the bald.

Abou *aïne*, the one with an eye.[121]

El *atsar*, the pusher.

El *dommar*, the strong-headed.

Abou *rokba*, the one with a neck.

Abou *quetaïa*, the hairy one.

El *besiss*, the impudent one.

El *mostahi*, the shame-faced one.

El *bekkaï*, the weeping one.

El *hezzaz*, the rummager.

El *lezzaz*, the unionist.

Abou *lâaba*, the expectorant.

El *fattache*, the searcher.

El *hakkak*, the rubber.

El *mourekhi*, the flabby one.

El *motelâ*, the ransacker.

El *mokcheuf*, the discoverer.

As regards the names of *kamera*[122] and *dekeur*, their meaning is plain. *Dekeur* is a word which signifies the male of all creatures, and is also used in the sense of 'mention' and 'memory'. When a man has met with an accident to his member, when it has been amputated, or has become weak, and he can, in consequence, no longer fulfil his conjugal duties, they say of him:

---

[121] The word *abou* signifies 'father,' and *abou aïne*, literally translated, means 'father of the eye,' But in reality the word used in this way indicates possession, and means 'who has.' See the *Chrestomathie Arabe* of Bresnier, page 67, second edition, note 2 of No. xv.

There are a great many similar combinations of words forming surnames or nicknames. Frequent recurrences in this sense will appear in this work.

[122] *Kamera* also signifies the 'gland of the penis.' The root of it, *kemeur*, means, 'to have a larger penis or gland than any other man,' and in a third form, 'rivalling anybody with respect to the size of the penis.'

'the member of such an one is dead;' which means: the remembrance of him will be lost, and his generation is cut off by the root. When he dies they will say, 'His member has been cut off,' meaning, 'His memory is departed from the world.'[123]

The *dekeur* plays also an important part in dreams. The man who dreams that his member has been cut off is certain not to live long after that dream, for, as said above, it presages the loss of his memory and the extinction of his race.

I shall treat this subject more particularly in the explication of dreams.[124]

The teeth (*senane*) represent years (*senine*); if therefore a man sees in a dream a fine set of teeth, this is for him the sign of a long life.

If he sees his nail (*defeur*) reversed or upside down, this is an indication that the victory (*defeur*) which he has gained over his enemies will change sides; and from a victor, he will become the vanquished; inversely, if he sees the nail of his enemy turned the wrong way, he can conclude that the victory which had been with his enemy will soon return to him.

The sight of a lily (*sonsana*) is the prognostication of a misfortune which will last a year (*son*, misfortune; *sena*, year).

The appearance of ostriches (*nâmate*) in dreams is of bad augury, because their name being formed of *nâa* and *mate*, signifies 'news of death,' namely, peril.

To dream of a shield (*henafa*) means the coming on of all sorts of misfortune, for this word, by a change of letters, gives *koul afa*, 'all bad luck.'

The sight of a fresh rose (*ouarde*) announces the arrival (*ouroud*) of a pleasure to make the heart tremble with joy;

---

[123] Note of the autograph edition: There is here a play of words respecting the different meanings of *dekeur*, and which it is impossible to give in English.

[124] The explication of these dreams turns generally upon words with several meanings, or upon references to the radical letters of which they are composed.

whilst a faded rose indicates deceitful news. It is the same with baldness of the temples, and similar things.[125]

The jessamine (*yasmine*) is formed of *yas*, signifying deception, or the happening of a thing contrary to your wish, and *mine*, which means untruth. The man, then, who sees a jessamine in his dream is to conclude that the deception, *yas*, in the name *yasmine*, is an untruth, and will thus be assured of the success of his enterprise.[126] However, the prognostications furnished by the jessamine have not the same character of certainty as those given by the rose. It differs, in fact, greatly from this latter flower, inasmuch as the slightest breath of wind will upset it.

The sight of a saucepan (*beurma*) announces the conclusion (*anuberame*) of affairs in which one is engaged. Abou Djahel[127] (God's curse be upon him!) has added that such conclusion would take place during the night.

A jar (*khabia*) is the sign of turpitude (*khebets*) in every kind of affair, unless it is one that has fallen into a pit or a river and got broken, so as to let escape all the calamities contained in it.

The sawing of wood (*nechara*) means good news (*bechara*).

The inkstand (*douaïa*) indicates the remedy (*doua*), namely, the cure of a malady, unless it be burnt, broken or lost, when it means the contrary.

The turban (*âmama*) if seen to fall over the face and covering the eyes is a presage of blindness (*âina*), from which God preserve us!

The finding again in good condition a gem that has been lost or forgotten is a sign of success.

If one dreams that he gets out of a window (*taga*) he may

[125] Some Mussulmans have the hairs plucked from the temples in order to look younger. This operation, which does not realise, in the eyes of strangers, the appearance of reality, is considered by the author as being like the announcement of lying news.

[126] This play of words upon jessamine is taken from the work of Azzedine el Mocadesi, called *The Birds and the Flowers*.

[127] Abou Djahel, one of the foremost men of the Koreïchites, was a sworn enemy of Mohammed and of his doctrine. His real name is Ameur ben Heïchame, of the family of Moukhzoum. He received also the surname of Abou el Heukoum, the man gifted with wisdom.

know that he will come with advantage out of all transactions he may have, whether important or not. But if the window seen in the dream is narrow so that he had some trouble to get out of it, this will be to him a sign that in order to be successful he will have to make efforts in proportion to the difficulty experienced by him in getting out.

The bitter orange signifies that from the place where it was seen calumnies will be issuing.[128]

Trees (*achedjar*) means discussions (*mechadjera*).

The carrot (*asefnaria*) prognosticates misfortune (*asef*) and sorrow.

The turnip (*cufte*) means for the man that has seen it a matter that is past and gone (*ameur fate*), so that there is no going back to it. The matter is weighty if it appeared large, of no importance if seen small; in short, important in proportion to the size of the turnip that has been seen.[129]

A musket seen without its being fired means a complot contrived in secret, and of no importance. But if it is seen going off it is a sign that the moment has arrived for the realisation of the complot.

The sight of fire is of bad augury.

If the pitcher (*brik*)[130] of a man who has turned to God breaks, this is a sign that his repentance is in vain, but if the glass out of which he drinks wine breaks, this means that he returns to God.

If you have dreamed of feasts and sumptuous banquets, be sure that quite contrary things will come to pass.

If you have seen somebody bidding adieu to people on their

---

[128] The connection no doubt originates with the fact that calumny bears bitter fruits, like the one in question.

[129] It must be confessed, looking at the forced relationship between *cufte* and *ameur fate*, that the author gets easily over any difficulties in his explanations of dreams.

[130] The *brik* is a small earthenware pitcher provided with a handle, which the Arab generally carries about with him filled with water for quenching his thirst. It has a peculiar shaped neck, which allows the water to be drunk easily.

going away you may be certain that it will be the latter who will
shortly wish him a good journey; for the poet says:

> If you have seen your friend saying good-bye, rejoice;
> Let your soul be content as to him who is far away,
> For you may look forward to his speedy return,
> And the heart of him who said adieu will come back to you.[131]

The coriander (*keusbeur*) signifies that the vulva (*keuss*) is in
proper condition.

On this subject there is a story that the Sultan Haroun er
Rachid having with him several persons of mark with whom he
was familiar, rose and left them to go to one of his wives, whom
he wanted to enjoy. He found her suffering from her courses,
and returned to his companions to sit down with them, resigned
to his disappointment.

Now it so happened that a moment afterwards the woman
found herself free from her discharge. When she had assured
herself of this, she made forthwith her ablutions, and sent to
the Sultan, by one of her negresses, a plate of coriander.[132]

Haroun er Rachid was seated amongst his friends when the
negress brought the plate to him. He took it and examined it,
but did not understand the meaning of its being sent to him
by his wife. At last he handed it to one of his poets, who, having
looked at it attentively, recited to him the following verses:

> She has sent you coriander (*keusbeur*),
> White as sugar;
> I have placed it in my palm,
> And concentrated all my thoughts upon it,
> In order to find out its meaning;
> And I have seized it. O my master, what she wants to say,
> Is 'My vulva is restored to health' (*keussi beuri*).

Er Rachid was surprised at the wit shown by the woman, and
at the poet's penetration. Thus that which was to remain a

---

[131] This is again a play of words by transposing letters, which the author
employs for explaining dreams, like the one given in Note 123 on p. 167. The
case here rests upon the words *âoud* and *oudaâ*, adieu.

[132] The coriander, *keusbeur*, preserves viands, as salt does. The viands,
dried and seasoned with spices, are called *kheliâ*. They will keep good
for a year, and longer. Coriander is, moreover, a stimulant.

mystery remained hidden, and that which was to be known was divulged.

A drawn sword is a sign of war, and the victory will remain with him who holds its hilt.

A bridle means servitude and oppression.

A long beard points to good fortune and prosperity; but it is said that it is a sign of death if it reaches down to the ground.

Others pretend that the intelligence of each man is in an inverse proportion to the length of his beard; that is to say, a big beard denotes a small mind. A story goes in this respect, that a man who had a long beard saw one day a book with the following sentence inscribed on its back: 'He whose chin is garnished with a large beard is as foolish as his beard is long.' Afraid of being taken for a fool by his acquaintances, he thought of getting rid of what there was too much of, and to this end, it being night-time, he grasped a handful of his beard close to the chin, and set the remainder on fire by the light of the lamp. The flame ran rapidly up the beard and reached his hand, which he had to withdraw precipitately on account of the heat. Thus his beard was burnt off entirely. Then he wrote on the back of the book, under the above mentioned sentence, 'These words are entirely true. I, who am now writing this, have proved their truth.' Being himself convinced that the weakness of the intellect is proportioned to the length of the beard.[133]

On the same subject it is related that Haroun er Rachid, being in a kiosk, saw a man with a long beard. He ordered the man to be brought before him, and when he was there he asked him, 'What is your name?' 'Abou Arouba,' replied the man.

'What is your profession?'

'I am a master in controversy.'

[133] This little tale brings out, not without humour, the double stupidity of the man who is its hero, and who, not content with burning off his whole beard, and probably also burning his skin, is writing down a certificate of his imbecility in the inscription which he adds with his own hand on the back of the book. One may, up to a certain point, discern here a connection between this demonstration and the famous argument: Epimenides says, 'That the Cretans are liars.' Now Epimenides is a Cretan.

Haroun then gave him the following case to solve. A man buys a he-goat, who, in voiding his excrements, hits the buyer's eye with part of it and injures the same. 'Who has to pay for damages?' 'The seller,' promptly says Abou Arouba. 'And why?' asked the Kalif. 'Because he has sold the animal without warning the buyer that it has a catapult in its anus,' answered the man. At these words the Kalif began to laugh immoderately, and recited the following verses:

> When the beard of the young man
> Has grown down to his navel,
> The shortness of his intellect is, in my eyes,
> Proportioned to the length his beard has grown.

It is averred by many authors that amongst proper names they are such as bring luck, and others that bring ill luck, according to the meaning they bear.

The names Ahmed, Mohammed, Hamdonna, Hamdoun, indicate in encounters and in dreams the lucky issue arrived at in a transaction.[134] Ali, Alia, indicate the height and elevation of rank.[135] Naserouna, Naseur, Mansour, Naseur Allah signify triumph over enemies.[136] Salem, Salema, Selim, Selimane indicate success in all affairs; also security for him who is in danger.[137] Fetah Allah, Fetah indicate victory, like all the other names which in their meaning speak of lucky things.[138] The names Râd, Râda signify thunder, tumult, and comprise everything in connection with this meaning.[139] Abou el Feurdj and Ferendj indicate joy; Ranem and Renime success, Khalf Allah and Khaleuf compensation for a loss, and benediction. The sense of Abder Rassi, Hafid and Mahfond is favourable. The names in which the words

[134] The root of these names is *hamd*, which means to praise, glorify, to bear oneself worthy of praise.

[135] The root is *ala*, signifying high, elevated both in reality and figuratively.

[136] From *neseur*, meaning to help, and by extension to carry off the victory. The word God is understood; helped by God is being victorious.

[137] From the root *selem*, which means to be right and well, to escape from a danger, to be safe.

[138] Ahmed, Mohammed, etc.

[139] The root *râd* signifies to thunder, menace as a verb; and tumult, trembling, misfortune, calamity as a substantive.

latif (benevolent), *mourits* (helpful), *hanine* (compassionate), *aziz* (beloved), carry with them, in conformity with the sense of these words, the ideas of benevolence, *lateuf* (charity), *iratsa* (compassion), *hanana*, and *aiz* (favour). As an example of words of an unfavourable omen I will cite *el ouar*, *el ouara*, which imply the idea of difficulties.

As supporting the truth of the preceding observations I will refer to this saying of the Prophet (the salutation and benevolence of God to him!). 'Compare the names appearing in your dreams with their signification, so that you may draw therefrom your conclusions.'[140]

I must confess that this was not the place for treating of this subject, but one word leads on to more. I now return to the object of this chapter, viz: the different names of the sexual parts of man.

The name of *el aïr* is derived from *el kir* (the smith's belows). In fact if you turn in the latter word the k, *kef*, so that it faces the opposite way, you will find the word to read *el aïr*.[141] The member is so called on account of its alternate swelling and subsiding again. If swollen up it stands erect, and if not it sinks down flaccid.

It is called *el hamama* (the pigeon), because after having been swelled out it resembles at the moment when it returns to repose a pigeon sitting on her eggs.[142]

El teunnana (the tinkler) – So called because every time it enters or comes out of the vulva in coition it makes a noise.

El heurmak (the indomitable)[143] – It has received this name because when in a state of erection it begins to move its head, searching for the entrance to the vulva till it has found it, and it then walks in quite insolently, without asking leave.

[140] See the *hadits*, or traditions left by Mohammed.
[141] This origin of the word air, although ingenious, is unlikely. It rests upon turning the Arab letter *kef*, preceded by the letter *lam* making it *lam alif*. It is thus that *kir*, turning the *kef* the other way, will read *aïr*.
[142] In Arabic the word which signifies eggs is also used for testicles, hence the comparison made by the author.
[143] *Heurmak* is not a common Arabian word. It signifies a fiery, violent indomitable stallion.

El ahlil (the liberator) – Thus called because in penetrating into the vulva of a woman thrice repudiated it gives her the liberty to return to her first husband.[144]

El zeub (the verge) – From the word *deub*, which means creeping. This name was given to the member because when it gets between a woman's thighs and feels a plump vulva it begins to creep upon the thighs and the Mount of Venus, then approaches the entrance of the vulva, and keeps creeping in until it is in possession and is comfortably lodged, and having it all its own way penetrates into the middle of the vulva, there to ejaculate.[145]

El hammache (the exciter) – It has received this name because it irritates the vulva by its frequent entries and exits.

El nâasse (the sleeper) – From its deceitful appearance. When it gets into erection, it lengthens out and stiffens itself to such an extent that one might think it would never get soft again. But when it has left the vulva, after having satisfied its passion, it goes to sleep.

There are members that fall asleep while inside the vulva, but the majority of them come out still firm; but at that moment they get drowsy, and little by little they go to sleep.

El zoddame (the crowbar) – It is called so because when it meets the vulva and the same will not let it pass in directly, it forces the entrance with its head, breaking and tearing everything, like a wild beast in the rutting season.

El khiate (the tailor) – It takes this name from the circumstance that it does not enter the vulva until it has manoeuvred about the entrance, like a needle in the hand of a tailor, creeping and rubbing against it until it is sufficiently roused, after which it enters.

Mochefi el relil (the extinguisher of passion) – This name is

[144] Note of the autograph edition: According to the Mussulman law a wife that has been divorced by the thrice repeated formula cannot marry her first husband again until she has married another man, and been divorced from him.

[145] In several passages of this work the man is advised when in coition to place his member well in the centre of the vagina at the crisis. The Arabian sages are not agreed upon the sense of this advice.

given to a member which is large, strong, and slow to ejaculate; such a member satisfies most completely the amorous wishes of a woman; for, after having wrought her up to the highest pitch, it allays her excitement better than any other. And, in the same way, it calms the ardour of the man. When it wants to get into the vulva, and arriving at the portal, finds it closed, it laments, begs and promises: 'Oh! my love! let me come in, I will not stay long.' And when it has been admitted, it breaks its word, and makes a long stay, and does not take its leave till it has satisfied its ardour by the ejaculation of the sperm, coming and going, tilting high and low, and rummaging right and left. The vulva protests, 'How about your word, you deceiver?' she says; 'you said you would only stop in for a moment.' And the member answers, 'Oh, certainly! I shall not retire till I have encountered your womb; but after having found it, I will engage to with-draw at once.' At these words, the vulva takes pity on him, and advances her matrix, which clasps and kisses its head, as if saluting it.[146] The member then retires with its passion cooled down.

El khorrate (the turnabout) – This name was given to it because on arriving at the vulva it pretends to come on important business, knocks at the door, turns about everywhere, without shame or bashfulness, investigating every corner to the right and left, forward and backward, and then all at once darts right to the bottom of the vagina for the ejaculation.

El deukkak (the striker) – Thus called because on arriving at the entrance of the vulva it gives a slight knock. If the vulva opens the door, it enters; if there is no response, it begins to knock again, and does not cease until it is admitted. The parasite[147]

---

[146] Note of the autograph edition : This image is drawn from a kind of salute very much in use by the lower class of Mussulmans when meeting a superior by seizing the head of the latter, and drawing it down so as to be able to kiss it.
[147] The word *teufil* of the text rendered in the translation with 'parasite' is the name of a man who lived in Coufa, an important town in Irak, and whom they had nicknamed *Teufil el Aaress*, the wedding teufil, because he always came to a wedding feast without invitation.

who wants to get into the house of a rich man to be present at a feast does the same: he knocks at the door; and if it is opened, he walks in; but if there is no response to his knock, he repeats it again and again until the door is opened. And similarly the *deukkak* with the door of the vulva.

By 'knocking at the door' is meant the friction of the member against the entrance of the vulva until the latter becomes moist. The appearance of this moisture is the phenomenon alluded to by the expression 'opening the door.'

El âouame (the swimmer) – Because when it enters the vulva it does not remain in one favourite place, but, on the contrary, turns to the right, to the left, goes forward, draws back, and then moves like swimming in the middle amongst its own sperm and the fluid furnished by the vulva, as if in fear of drowning and trying to save itself.

El dekhal (the housebreaker) – Merits that name because on coming to the door of the vulva this one asks, 'What do you want?' 'I want to come in!' 'Impossible! I cannot take you in on account of your size.' Then the member insists that the other one should only receive its head, promising not to come in entirely; it then approaches, rubs its head twice or thrice between the vulva's lips, till they get humid and thus lubricated, then introduces first its head, and after, with one push, plunges in up to the testicles.

El aâouar (the one-eyed) – Because it has but one eye, which eye is not like other eyes, and does not see clearly.[148]

El fortass (the bald one) – Because there is no hair on its head, which makes it look bald.

Abou aïne (he with one eye) – It has received this name because its one eye presents the peculiarity of being without pupil and eyelashes.

El âtsar (the stumbler) – It is called so because if it wants to penetrate in the vulva, as it does not see the door, it beats about above and below, and thus continues to stumble as over stones

[148] The epithet of one-eyed is also given by Martial to the virile member.

in the road, until the lips of the vulva get humid, when it manages to get inside. The vulva then says, 'What has happened to you that made you stumble about so?' The member answers, 'O my love, it was a stone lying in the road.'

El dommar (the odd-headed) – Because its head is different from all other heads.

Abou rokba (the one with a neck) – That is the being with a short neck, a well developed throat, and thick at the end, a bald head, and who, moreover, has coarse and bristly hair from the navel to the pubis.

Abou guetaïa (the hairy one; who has a forest of hair) – This name is given to it when the hair is abundant about it.

El besiss (the impudent) – It has received this name because from the moment that it gets stiff and long it does not care for anybody, lifts impudently the clothing of its master by raising its head fiercely, and makes him ashamed while itself feels no shame. It acts in the same unabashed way with women, turning up their clothes and laying bare their thighs. Its master may blush at this conduct, but as to itself its stiffness and determination to plunge into a vulva only increase.

El mostahi (the shame-faced) – This sort of member which is met with sometimes, is capable of feeling ashamed and timid when facing a vulva which it does not know, and it is only after a little time that it gets bolder and stiffens. Sometimes it is even so much troubled that it remains incompetent for the coitus, which happens in particular when a stranger is present, in which case it becomes quite incapable of moving.

El bekkai (the weeper) – So called on account of the many tears it sheds; as soon as it gets in erection, it weeps; when it sees a pretty face, it weeps; handling a woman, it weeps. It goes even so far as to weep tears sacred to memory.

El hezzaz (the rummager) – It is named thus because as soon as it penetrates into the vulva it begins to rummage about vigorously, until it has appeased its passion.

El lezzaz (the unionist) – Received that name because as soon

M

as it is in the vulva it pushes and works till fur meets fur, and even makes efforts to force the testicles into it.

Abou lâaba (the expectorant) – Has received this name because when coming near a vulva, or when it sees one, or even when merely thinking of it, or when its master touches a woman or plays with her or kisses her, its saliva begins to move and it has tears in its eye; this saliva is particularly abundant when it has been for some time out of work, and it will even wet then his master's dress. This member is very common, and there are but few people who are not furnished with it.

The liquid it sheds is cited by lawyers under the name of *medi*.[149] Its production is the result of toyings and of lascivious thoughts. With some people it is so abundant as to fill the vulva, so that they may erroneously believe that it comes from the woman.

El fattache (the searcher) – From its habit, when in the vulva, of turning in every direction as if in search of something; and that something is the matrix. It will know no rest until it has found it.

El hakkak (the rubber) – It has got this name because it will not enter the vagina until it has rubbed its head against the entrance and the lower part of the belly. It is frequently mistaken for the next one.

El mourekhi (the flabby one) – The one who can never get in because it is too soft, and which is therefore content to rub its head against the entrance to the vulva until it ejaculates. It gives no pleasure to woman, but only inflames her passion without being able to satisfy it, and makes her cross and irritable.

El motelâ (the ransacker) – So named because it penetrates into unusual places, makes itself well acquainted with the state of vulvas, and can distinguish their qualities and faults.

El mokcheuf (the discoverer) – Has been thus denominated because in getting up and raising its head, it raises the vestments

---

[149] Note of the autograph edition: *Medi*, sperm exuding by the mere touching of a woman.—*Dictionary of Kazimirski*, page 182. No doubt the prostatic moisture is alluded to here.

which hide it, and uncovers its master's nudities, and because it is also not afraid to lay bare the vulvas which it does not yet know, and to lift up the clothes which cover them without shame. It is not accessible to any sense of bashfulness, cares for nothing and respects nothing. Nothing which concerns the coitus is strange to it; it has a profound knowledge of the state of humidity, freshness, dryness, tightness or warmth of vulvas, which it explores assiduously. There are, in fact, certain vulvas of an exquisite exterior, plump and fine outside, while their inside leaves much to wish for, and they give no pleasure, owing to their being not warm, but very humid, and having other similar faults. It is for this reason that the *mokcheuf* tries to find out about things concerning the coitus, and has received this name.

These are the principal names that have been given to the virile member according to its qualities. Those who think that the number of these names is not exhaustive can look for more; but I think I have given a nomenclature long enough to satisfy my readers.

CHAPTER IX

Sundry Names given to the Sexual Organs of Women [150]

El *feurdj*, the slit.

El *keuss*, the vulva.

El *kelmoune*, the voluptuous.

El *ass*, the primitive.

El *zerzour*, the starling.

El *cheukk*, the chink.

Abou *tertour*, the one with a crest. [151]

Abou *khochime*, the one with a little nose.[151]

El *gueunfond*, the hedgehog.

El *sakouti*, the silent one.

El *deukkak*, the crusher.

El *tseguil*, the importunate.

El *taleb*, the yearning one.

[150] Here are some of the names given by Rabelais to the natural parts of women; *le serrecropière, le calibistris, le pertuys, le boursavitz.*—Apollinaire's edition of Aretino (Paris, Bibliothèque des Curieux, 2 vols., 1909-10) employs the word *pertuis* ('pertuys'), particularly in the *Sonnetti Lussuriosi* (*Sonnets Luxurieux*, vol. I of the above edition). (A.H.W.)

[151] The word *abou* signifies father, and *abou aïne* literally translated means 'father of the eye,' but in reality the word used in this way indicates the possession, and means, 'who has'—See the *Crestomathie Arabe* of Bresnier, page 67, second edition, note 2 of No. xv. There are a great many similar combinations of words forming surnames or nicknames. Frequent recurrences in this sense will appear in this work.

El *hacene*, the beautiful.

El *neuffakh*, the one that swells.

Abou *djebaha*, the one with a projection.[152]

Elouasâ, the vast one.

El *dride*, the large one.

Abou *beldoum*, the glutton.[152]

El *mokaour*, the bottomless.

Abou *cheufrine*, the two lipped.[152]

Abou *âungra*, the humpbacked.[152]

El *rorbal*, the sieve.

El *hezzaz*, the restless.

El *lezzaz*, the unionist.

El *moudd*, the accommodating.

El *moudïne*, the assistant.

El *meusboul*, the long one.

El *molki*, the duellist.

El *harrab*, the fugitive.

El *sabeur*, the resigned.

El *moseuffah*, the barred one.

El *mezour*, the deep one.

El *addad*, the biter.

El *menssass*, the sucker.

El *zeunbur*, the wasp.

El *harr*, the hot one.

El *ladid*, the delicious one.

As regards the vulva called *el feurdj*, the slit, it has this name because it opens and shuts again when hotly yearning for coitus, like the one of a mare in heat at the approach of the stallion. This word, however, is applied indiscriminately to the natural parts of men and women, for God the Supreme has used this expression in the Koran, chap. xxxiii. v. 35, 'El *hafidine*

[152] See note 151 on preceding page.

feuroudjahoum ou el hafidate.'[153] The proper meaning of *feurdj*
is slit, opening, passage; people say 'I have found a *feurdj* in the
mountains,' viz., a passage; there is then a *soukoune* upon the
ra and a *fatcha* upon the *djïne*, and in this sense it means also the
natural parts of woman. But if the *ra* is marked with a *fatcha*
it signifies deliverance from misfortunes. [154]

The person who dreams of having seen the vulva, *feurdj*, of a
woman will know that 'if he is in trouble God will free him of it;
if he is in a perplexity he will soon get out of it; and lastly if
he is in poverty he will soon become wealthy, because *feurdj*, by
transposing the vowels, will mean the deliverance from evil. By
analogy, if he wants a thing he will get it; if he has debts, they
will be paid.'

It is considered more lucky to dream of the vulva as open. But
if the one seen belongs to a young virgin it indicates that the
door of consolation will remain closed, and the thing which is
desired is not obtainable. It is a proved fact that the man who sees
in his dream the vulva of a virgin that has never been touched
will certainly be involved in difficulties, and will not be lucky
in his affairs. But if the vulva is open so that he can look well
into it, or even if it is hidden but he is free to enter it, he will
bring the most difficult tasks to a successful end after having
first failed in them, and this after a short delay, by the help of
a person whom he never thought of.

He who has seen in his dream a man busy upon a young girl,
and when the same is getting off her managed to see at that
moment her vulva, will bring his business to a happy end, after
having first failed to do so, by the help of the man he has seen.
If it is himself who did the girl's business, and he has seen her
vulva, he will succeed by his own exertions to realize the most

[153] The literal translation is, 'men and women who are sparing with their
sexual organs,' *feurdj* being rendered by sexual organ. This quotation
really proves that the word *feurdj* applies to both the sexes. The passage
may be translated, 'the persons of both sexes who are chaste,' and is thus
given in the Koran translation of Kazimirski.

[154] In Arabic, words composed of the same letters may bear different
meaning according to the marks, which affect their vowels.

difficult problems, and be successful in every respect. Generally speaking, to see the vulva in dreams is a good sign; so it is of good augury to dream of coition, and he who sees himself in the act, and finishing with the ejaculation, will meet success in all his affairs. But it is not the same with the man who merely begins coition and does not finish it. He, on the contrary, will be unlucky in every enterprise.

It is supposed that the man who dreams of being busy with a woman will afterwards obtain from her what he wants.

The man who dreams of cohabiting with women with whom to have sexual intercourse is forbidden by religion, as for instance his mother, sister, etc., (*maharine*), must consider this as a presage that he will go to sacred places (*moharreme*); and, perhaps, even journey to the holy house of God, and look there upon the grave of the Prophet.[155]

As regards the virile member, it has been previously mentioned that to dream of accident occurring to that organ means the loss of all remembrance and the extinction of the race.

The sight of a pair of pantaloons (*seronal*) prognosticates the appointment to a place (*oulaïa*), by reason of the analogy of the letters composing the word *seronal* with those forming by transposition the two words *sir*, go, and *ouali*, named : 'go to the post to which you are named.' It is related that a man who had dreamed that the Emir had given him a pair of pantaloons became Cadi. Dreaming of pantaloons is also a sign of protection for the natural parts, and foretells success in business.

The almond (*louze*), a word composed of the same letters as *zal*, to cease, seen in a dream by a man in trouble means that he will be liberated from it; to a man who is ill, that he will be cured; in short that all misfortunes will give way. Somebody having dreamed that he was eating almonds, asked a wise man the meaning of it; he received the answer, that by reason of the

---

[155] The word *harame* signifies at the same time illicit, forbidden action, and a holy thing. *Moharreme* indicates the holy soil of Mecca, the place of pilgrimage for Mussulmans. *Maharime* designates the persons whom to enjoy in coition is prohibited by religion.

analogy of the letters in *louze* and *zal*, the ills that beset him would disappear; and the event justified the explanation.

The sight of a molar tooth (*deurss*) in a dream indicates enmity. The man, therefore, who has seen his tooth drop out may be sure that his enemy is dead. This arises from the word *deurss*, signifying both an enemy and a molar, and one can say at the same time, 'It is my tooth and it is my enemy.'[156]

The window (*taga*)[157] and the shoe (*medassa*) reminds you of women. The vulva resembles in fact, when invaded by the verge, a window with a man putting his head in to look about, or a shoe that is being put on. Consequently, he who sees himself in dreaming in the act of getting in at a window, or putting on a shoe, has the certainty of getting possession of a young woman or a virgin, if the window is newly built, or the shoe new and in good condition; but that the woman will be old according to the state of the window or shoe.

The loss of a shoe foretells to a man the loss of his wife.

To dream of something folded together, and which gets open, predicts that a secret will be divulged and made public. The same remaining folded up indicates, on the other hand, that the secret will be kept.

If you dream of reading a letter you will know that you will have news, which will be, according to the nature of the contents of the letter, good or bad.

The man who dreams of passages in the Koran or the Traditions, *Hadits*, will from the subjects treated therein draw his conclusions. For instance the passage, 'He will grant you the help of God and immediate victory,' will signify to him victory and triumph. 'Certainly he (God) has the decision in his hands.' 'Heaven will open and offer its numerous portals.' And other similar passages indicate success.

A passage treating of punishments prognosticates punishment;

---

[156] *Deurss* signifies a molar tooth and a man difficult to live with, hence enemy.

[157] The Arabs use sometimes in joke the word *taga* (window) for designating the sexual organ of woman.

from those treating of benefits a lucky event may be concluded. Such is the passage in the Koran, which says: 'He who forgives sins is terrible in his inflictions.'[158]

Dreams about poetry and songs contain their explanation in the contents of the objects of the dream.

He who dreams of horses, mules, or asses may hope for good, for the Prophet (God's salutation and goodness be with him!) has said, 'Men's fortunes are attached to the forelocks of their horses till the day of resurrection!' and it is written in the Koran, 'God the Highest has thus willed it that they serve you for mounts and for state.'[159]

The correctness of these prognostications is not subject to any doubt.

He who dreams of seeing himself mounted upon an ass as a courier, and arriving at his destination, will be lucky in all things; but he who tumbles off the ass on his way is advised that he will be subject to accidents and misfortunes.

The fall of the turban from the head predicts ignominy, the turban being the Arabs' crown.

If you see yourself in a dream with naked feet it means a loss; and the bare head has the same significance.

By transposing the letters other analogies may be arrived at.

These explanations are not here in their place; but I have been induced to give them in this chapter on account of the use to which they may be put. Persons who would wish to know more on this subject have only to consult the treatise of Ben Sirine. I now return to the names given to the sexual parts of woman.

---

[158] 'Who effaces sins, welcomes repentance, and who is terrible in punishments.' Koran, chap. xi, v. 2.—See also Rodwell's *Koran*, Everyman Edition (1939), page 290 (*Sura* 35): 'The good word riseth up to Him, and the righteous deed will He exalt. But a severe punishment awaiteth the plotters of evil things; and the plots of such will He render vain.' (A.H.W.)

[159] 'Il' (God) has given you horses, mules, and asses to serve you as mounts and for pomp. He has created what you do not doubt.' Koran, chap. xvi, v. 8.

El keuss (the vulva)[160] – This word serves as the name of a young woman's vulva in particular. Such a vulva is very plump and round in every direction, with long lips, grand slit, the edges well divided and symmetrical and rounded; it is soft, seductive, perfect throughout. It is the most pleasant and no doubt the best of all the different sorts. May God grant us the possession of such a vulva! Amen. It is warm, tight, and dry; so much so that one might expect to see fire burst out from it. Its form is graceful, its odour pleasant; the whiteness of its outside sets off its carmine-red middle. There is no imperfection about it.

El relmoune (the voluptuous)[161] – The name given to the vulva of a young virgin.

El ass (the primitive) – This is a name applicable to every kind of vulva.

El zerzour (the starling) – The vulva of a very young girl, or, as others pretend, of a brunette.

El cheukk (the chink) – The vulva of a bony, lean woman. It is like a chink in a wall, with not a vestige of flesh. May God keep us from it!

[160] The word *keuss*, signifying the natural parts of woman, is not an original Arabic word; it is derived from the ancient Greek.

[161] Note of the autograph edition: All the qualifications given in the Arab text to the sexual organs of woman have reference to the word *feurdj*, which is used as masculine, and is translated with vulva and vagina. In order to avoid a fatiguing repetition of one and the same word, the translator has used now one, now the other of these expressions, which has occasioned the following anomaly: the Arab word *feurdj* is always masculine, while of the French words for vulva and vagina the first, *vulve*, is feminine, and the other, *vagin*, is masculine. We must observe here that neither vulva nor vagina give exactly the sense of the Arab *feurdj*, which designates the whole of the organ for copulation of the woman, whilst vulva means the outside parts up to the membrane, and vagina is the conduit destined for the reception of the virile member up to the matrix. Neither of these words, therefore, corresponds exactly to *feurdj*; that as it was not feasible to use in the descriptions a long paraphrase, as 'the organ for copulation in woman,' and still less the vulgar latin word *cunnus*, it has seemed more convenient to apply the rhetorical figure called *synecdoche*, *viz.*, to designate the whole by a part, and to use in turns the two above mentioned words, but vulva in preference with respect to the outer parts, and vagina when the interior parts are spoken of.

Abou tertour (the crested one)[162] – It is the name given to a vulva furnished with a red comb, like that of a cock, which rises at the moment of enjoyment.

Abou khochime (the snubnose) – Is a vulva with thin lips and a small tongue.[163]

El gueunfond (the hedgehog) – The vulva of the old, decrepit woman, dried up with age and with bristly hair.

El sakouti (the silent one) – This name has been given to the vulva that is noiseless. The member may enter it a hundred times a day but it will not say a word, and will be content to look on without a murmur.

El deukkak (the crusher) – So called from its crushing movements upon the member. It generally begins to push the member, directly it enters, to the right and to the left, and to grip it with the matrix, and would, if it could, absorb also the two testicles.

El tseguil (the importunate) – This is the vulva which is never tired of taking in the member. This latter might pass a hundred nights with it, and walk in a hundred times every night, still that vulva would not be sated – nay, it would want still more, and would not allow the member to come out again at all, if it was possible. With such a vulva the parts are exchanged; the vulva is the pursuer, the member the pursued.[164] Luckily it is a rarity, and only found in a small number of women, who are wild with passion, all on fire, and in flame.

El taleb (the yearning one) – This vagina is met with in a few women only. With some it is natural; with others it becomes what it is by long abstinence. It is burning for a member, and, having got one in its embrace, it refuses to part with it until its fire is completely extinguished.

---

[162] There is no doubt that the author wanted to designate by comb that part of the sexual organs of woman which is called *clitoris*, from the Greek, *kleitoris*.

[163] The small lips, or nymphs, are spoken of here, which, in young girls, are hidden by the larger ones.

[164] Note in the autograph edition: The author used two expressions belonging to the law, *el mentloub* and *el taleb*, signifying the defendant and the plaintiff.

El hacene (the beautiful) – This is the vulva which is white, plump, in form vaulted like a dome, firm, and without any deformity. You cannot take your eyes off it, and to look at it changes a feeble erection into a strong one.

El neuffakh (the swelling one) – So called because a torpid member coming near it, and rubbing its head against it a few times, at once swells and stands upright. To the woman who has such a one it procures excessive pleasure, for, at the moment of the crisis, it opens and shuts convulsively, like the vulva of a mare.

Abou djebaha (one with a projection) – Some women have this sort of vulva, which is very large, with a pubis prominent like a projecting, fleshy forehead.

El ouasa (the vast one) – A vulva surrounded by a very large pubis. Women of that build are said to be of large vagina, because, although on the approach of the member it appears firm and impenetrable to such a degree that not even a *meroud*[165] seems likely to be passed in, as soon as it feels the friction of the glans against its centre it opens wide at once.

El aride (the large one) – This is the vulva which is as wide as it is long; that is to say, fully developed all round, from side to side, and from the pubis to the perineum. It is the most beautiful to look upon. As the poet has said :

> It has the splendid whiteness of a forehead,
> In its dimensions it is like the moon,
> The fire that radiates from it is like the sun's,
> And seems to burn the member which approaches;
> Unless first moistened with saliva the member cannot enter,
> The odour it emits is full of charms.

It is also said that this name applies to the vagina of women who are plump and fat. When such a one crosses her thighs one over the other the vulva stands out like the head of a calf.

---

[165] Note to the autograph edition : The *meroud* is a little stick or stylus which the Arabian women use for blackening their eyelids, or for introducing an eye salve.

If she lays it bare it resembles a saâ[166] for corn placed between her thighs; and, if she walks, it is apparent under her clothes by its wavy movement at each step. May God, in his goodness and generosity, let us enjoy such a vagina! It is of all the most pleasing, the most celebrated, the most wished for.

Abou belâoum (the glutton) – The vulva with a vast capacity for swallowing. If such a vulva has not been able to get coitus for some time it fairly engulfs the member that then comes near it, without leaving any trace of it outside, like as a man who is famished flings himself upon viands that are offered to him, and would swallow them without mastication.

El mokâour (the bottomless) – This is the vagina of indefinite length, having, in consequence, the matrix lying very far back. It requires a member of the largest dimensions; any other could not succeed in rousing its amorous sensibilities.

Abou cheufrine (the two lipped) – This name is given to the amply developed vagina of an excessively stout woman. Also to the vagina the lips of which having become flaccid, owing to weakness, are long and pendulous.

Abou âungra (the humpbacked) – This vulva has the mount of Venus prominent and hard, standing out like the hump on the back of the camel, and reaching down between the thighs like the head of a calf. May God let us enjoy such a vulva! Amen!

El rorbal (the sieve) – This vulva on receiving a member seems to sift it all over, below, right and left, fore and aft, until the moment of pleasure arrives.

El hezzaz (the restless) – When this vagina has received the member it begins to move violently and without interruption until the member touches the matrix, and then knows no repose till it has hastened on the enjoyment and finished its work.

El lezzaz (the unionist) – The vagina which, having taken in

---

[166] Note to autograph edition: The *saâ* is a measure for cereals, and which will contain, according to the localities in which it is used, different quantities, from three to eight décalitres. It is certain that the author in making this comparison had in view the round form of the sack containing the grain, and not the volume of a *saâ*.

the member, clings to it and pushes itself forward upon it so closely that, if the thing were possible, it would enfold the two testicles.

El moudd (the accommodating) – This name is applied to the vagina of a woman who has felt for a long time an ardent wish for coition. In rapture with the member it sees, it is glad to second its movements of come and go; it offers its matrix to the member by pressing it forward within reach, which is, after all, the best gift it can offer. Whatever place inside of it the member wants to explore, this vulva will make him welcome to, gracefully according to its wish; there is no corner it will not help the member to reach.

El mouãïne (the assistant) – This vulva is thus named because it assists the member to go in and out, to go up and down, in short, in all its movements, in such a way that if it desires to do a thing, to enter or to retire, to move about, etc., the vulva hastens to give it all facilities, and answers to its appeal. By this aid the ejaculation is facilitated, and the enjoyment heightened.

El meusboul (the long one) – This name applies only to some vulvas; everyone knows that vulvas are far from being all of the same conformation and aspect. This vulva extends from the pubis to the anus. It lengthens out when the woman is lying down or standing, and contracts when she is sitting, differing in this respect from the vulva of a round shape. It looks like a splendid cucumber lying between the thighs.[167] With some women it shows projecting under light clothing, or when they are bending back.

El molki (the duellist) – This is the vulva which, on the introduction of a member, executes the movement of coming and going, pushes itself upon it for fear of its retiring before the pleasure arrives. There is no enjoyment for it but the shock

[167] Note in the autograph edition: This comparison of the vulva to a cucumber cannot seem otherwise than ridiculous to us, nevertheless it is often used by the Arabs. It serves to designate a vulva gifted with qualities which make it desirable.

given to its matrix by the member, and it is for this that it projects its matrix to grip and suck the member's gland when the ejaculation takes place. Certain vulvas, wild with desire and lust, be it natural or a consequence of long abstention, throw themselves upon the approaching member, opening the mouth like a famished infant to whom the mother offers the breast. In the same way this vulva advances and retires upon the member to bring it face to face with the matrix, as if in fear that, unaided, it could not find the same.

The vulva and the member resemble thus two skilful duellists, each time that one of them rushes upon its antagonist, the latter opposes its shield to parry the blow and repulse the assault. The member represents the sword, and the matrix the shield. The one who first ejaculates the sperm is vanquished; while the one who is slowest is the victor; and, assuredly, it is a fine fight! I should like thus to fight without stopping to the day of my death.

As the poet says:

> I have let them see the effect of a subtle shadow,
> Spinning like an ever busy spider.
> They said to me, 'How long will you go on?'
> I answered them, 'I will work till I am dead.'

El harrab (the fugitive) – The vagina which, being very tight and short, is hurt by the penetration of a very large and stiff member; it tries to escape to the right and left. It is thus, people say, with the vagina of most virgins, which, not yet having made the acquaintance of the member and fearful of its approach, tries to get out of its way, when it glides in between the thighs and wants to be admitted.

El sabeur (the resigned) – This is the vulva which, having admitted the member, submits patiently to all its whims and movements. It is also said that this vulva is strong enough to suffer resignedly the most violent and prolonged coitions. If it were assaulted a hundred times it would not be vexed or annoyed; and instead of venting reproaches, it would give thanks to God.

It will show the same patience if it has to do with several members who visit it successively.

This kind of vagina is found in women of a glowing temperament. If they only knew how to do it, they would not allow the man to dismount, nor his member to retire for a single moment.

El moseuffah (the barred one) – This kind of vagina is not often met with. The defect which distinguishes it is sometimes natural, sometimes it is the result of an unskilfully executed operation of circumcision upon the woman.[168] It can happen that the operator makes a false move with his instrument and injures the two lips, or even only one of them. In healing there forms a thick scar, which bars the passage, and in order to make the vagina accessible to the member, a surgical operation and the use of the bistouri will have to be resorted to.

El merour (the deep one) – The vagina which always has the mouth open, and the bottom of which is beyond sight. The longest members only can reach it.

El âddad (the biter) – The vulva which, when the member has got into it and is burning with passion, opens and shuts again upon the same fiercely. It is chiefly when the ejaculation is coming that the man feels the head of his member bitten by the mouth of the matrix. And certainly there is an attractive power in the same when it clings, yearning for sperm, to the gland, and draws it in as far as it can. If God in his power has decreed that the woman shall become pregnant the sperm gets concentrated in the matrix, where it is gradually vivified; but if, on the contrary, God does not permit the conception, the matrix expels the seed, which then runs over the vagina.

El meusass (the sucker) – This is a vagina which in its amorous heat in consequence of voluptuous toyings, or of long abstinence,

---

[168] Note of the autograph edition: In certain countries in Africa an operation is made upon girls, analogous to circumcision, consisting in the partial excision of the lesser lips of the vulva, which attain in that climate a sometimes disproportional development. (*Dictionnaire de Médecine*, Littré et Robin, page 306.)

begins to suck the member which has entered it so forcibly as to deprive it of all its sperm, dealing with it as a child drawing on the breast of the mother.

The poets have described it in the following verses:

> She – the woman – shows in turning up her robe
> An object – the vulva – developed full and round,
> In semblance like a cup turned upside down.
> In placing thereupon your hand, you seem to feel
> A well formed bosom, springy, firm, and full.
> In boring in your lance it gets well bitten,
> And drawn in by a suction, as the breast is by a child.
> And after having finished, if you wish to re-commence,
> You'll find it flaming hot as any furnace.

Another poet (may God grant all his wishes in Paradise!) has composed on the same theme the following lines:

> Like to a man extended on his chest, she – the vulva – fills the hand
> Which has to be well stretched to cover it.
> The place it occupies is standing forth
> Like an unopened bud of the blossom of a palm tree.
> Assuredly the smoothness of its skin
> Is like the beardless cheek of adolescence;
> Its conduit is but narrow,
> The entrance to it is not easy,
> And he who essays to get in
> Feels as though he was butting against a coat of mail.
> And at the introduction it emits a sound
> Like to the tearing of a woven stuff.
> The member having filled its cavity,
> Receives the lively welcome of a bite,
> Such as the nipple of the nurse receives
> When placed between the nursling's lips for suction.
> Its lips are burning,
> Like a fire that is lighted,
> And how sweet it is, this fire!
> How delicious for me.

El zeunbour (the wasp) – This kind of vulva is known by the strength and roughness of its fur. When the member approaches and tries to enter it gets stung by the hairs as if by a wasp.

El harr (the hot one) – This is one of the most praiseworthy vulvas. Warmth is in fact very much esteemed in a vulva, and

N

it may be said that the intensity of the enjoyment afforded by
it is in proportion to the heat it develops.

Poets have praised it in the following verses:

> The vulva possesses an intrinsic heat;
> Shut in a solid heart (interior) and pent up breast (matrix).
> Its fire communicates itself to him that enters it;
> It equals in intensity the fire of love.
> She is as tight as a well-fitting shoe,[169]
> Smaller than the circle of the apple of the eye.

El ladid (the delicious) — It has the reputation of procuring
an unexampled pleasure, comparable only to the one felt by the
beasts and birds of prey, and for which they fight sanguinary
combats. And if such effects are produced upon animals, what
must they be for man? And so it is that all wars spring from
the search of the voluptuous pleasure which the vagina procures,
and which is the highest fortune of this world; it is a part of the
delights of paradise awarded to us by God as a foretaste of what
is waiting for us, namely, delights a thousand times superior,
and above which only the sight of the Benevolent (God) is to be
placed.

More names might certainly be found applicable to the sexual
organs of woman, but the number of those mentioned above
appears to me ample. The principal object of this work is to
collect together all the remarkable and attractive matters concerning coitus, so that he who is in trouble may find consolation in it, and the man to whom erection offers difficulties
may be able to look into it for a remedy against his weakness.
Wise physicians have written that people whose members have
lost their strength, and are afflicted with impotence, should
assiduously read books treating of coition, and study carefully
the different kind of lovemaking, in order to recover their former
vigour. A certain means of provoking erection is to look at

---

[169] Note of the autograph edition: This comparison is somewhat vulgar
for poetry, and may even appear incomprehensible; nevertheless it finds
its explanation in the fact that the shoes of the Arabs are kept fast to the
foot by their upper borders being narrower than the foot itself, which
has to be forced in.

animals in the act of coition. As it is not always everywhere possible to see animals whilst in the act of copulation, books on the subject of generation are indispensable. In every country, large or small, both the rich and poor have a taste for this sort of book, which may be compared to the stone of philosophy transforming common metals into gold.[170]

It is related (and God penetrates the most obscure matters, and is most wise!) that once upon a time, before the reign of the great Kalif Haroun er Rachid, there lived a buffoon, who was the amusement of women, old people and children. His name was Djoâidi.[171] Many women granted him their favours freely, and he was much liked and well received by all. By princes, vizirs and caïds he was likewise very well treated; in general all the world pampered him; at that time, indeed, any man that was a buffoon enjoyed the greatest consideration, for which reason the poet has said:

> Oh, Time! Of all the dwellers here below
> You only elevate buffoons or fools,
> Or him whose mother was a prostitute,
> Or him whose anus as an inkstand[172] serves,
> Or him who from his youth has been a pander;
> Who has no other work but to bring the two sexes together.

Djoâidi related the following story:

The History of Djoâidi and Fadehat el Djemal

I was in love with a woman who was all grace and perfection, beautiful of shape, and gifted with all imaginable charms. Her cheeks were like roses, her forehead lily white, her lips like

[170] There always has been, and probably always will be, a demand for erotic literature, whether of an instructional type, such as the present work, or whether fictional, boudoir, or purely aphrodisiacal. The remarks of the Shaykh concerning the need for such literature reveal acumen, reinforced by practical common-sense. (A.H.W.)

[171] *Djoâidi* signifies a man of the people. The root *djâa* points to crisp naturally curling hair.

[172] Note in the autograph edition: Paraphrase for a designing minion, a giton. It takes its origin from the comparison, very common with the Arabs, of the pen and the inkstand and the verge and the vulva.

coral; she had teeth like pearls, and breasts like pomegranates. Her mouth opened round like a ring; her tongue seemed to be incrusted with precious gems; her eyes, black and finely slit, had the languor of slumber, and her voice the sweetness of sugar. With her form pleasantly filled out, her flesh was mellow like fresh butter, and pure as the diamond.

As to her vulva, it was white, prominent, round as an arch; the centre of it was red, and breathed fire, without a trace of humidity; for, sweet to the touch, it was quite dry. When she walked it showed in relief like a dome or an inverted cup. In reclining it was visible between her thighs, looking like a kid couched on a hillock.

This woman was my neighbour. All the others played and laughed with me, jested with me, and met my suggestions with great pleasure. I revelled in their kisses, their close embraces and nibblings, and in sucking their lips, breasts, and necks. I had coition with all of them, except my neighbour, and it was exactly her I wanted to possess in preference to all the rest; but instead of being kind to me, she avoided me rather. When I contrived to take her aside to trifle with her and try to rouse her gaiety, and spoke to her of my desires, she recited to me the following verses, the sense of which was a mystery to me :

> Among the mountain tops I saw a tent placed firmly,
> Apparent to all eyes high up in mid-air.
> But, oh ! the pole that held it up was gone.
> And like a vase without a handle it remained,
> With all its cords undone, its centre sinking in,
> Forming a hollow like that of a kettle.

Every time I told her of my passion she answered me with these verses, which to me were void of meaning, and to which I could make no reply, which, however, only excited my love all the more. I therefore inquired of all those I knew – amongst wise men, philosophers, and savants – the meaning, but not one of them could solve the riddle for me, so as to satisfy my heat and appease my passion.

Nevertheless I continued my investigations, when at last I

heard of a savant named Abou Nouass,[173] who lived in a far-off
country, and who, I was told, was the only man capable of solv-
ing the enigma. I betook myself to him, apprised him of the
discourses I had with the woman, and recited to him the above-
mentioned verses.

Abou Nouass said to me, 'This woman loves you to the
exclusion of every other man. She is very corpulent and plump.'
I answered, 'It is exactly as you say. You have given her likeness
as if she were before you, excepting what you say in respect of
her love for me, for, until now, she has never given me any
proof of it.'

'She has no husband.'

'This is so,' I said.

Then he added, 'I have reason to believe that your member
is of small dimensions, and such a member cannot give her
pleasure nor quench her fire; for what she wants is a lover with
a member like that of an ass. Perhaps it may not be so. Tell me the
truth about this!' When I had reassured him on that point,
affirming that my member, which began to rise at the expression
of his doubtings, was full-sized, he told me that in that case all
difficulties would disappear, and explained to me the sense of
the verses as follows:

The *tent*, firmly planted, represents the vulva of grand
dimension and placed well forward, the *mountains*, between
which it rises, are the thighs. The *stake* which supported its
centre and has been torn up, means that she has no husband,
comparing the stake or pole that supports the tent to the virile
member holding up the lips of the vulva. *She is like a vase without a handle*; this means if the pail is without a handle to hang it
up by it is good for nothing, the pail representing the vulva, and

---

[173] The real name of Abou Nouass was Abou Ali Hacene. He also had
the surname el Hakemi. He was born of obscure parents towards 135 or
136 of the Hegira, and acquired a great reputation as a poet and a philosopher.—He was also notorious as a paederast, and not a few of his poems
are of a homosexual character. See Burton's remarks concerning him in
various places in *The Arabian Nights*. (A.H.W.)

the handle the verge. *The cords are undone and its centre is sinking in;* that is to say, as the tent without a supporting pole caves in at the centre, inferior in this respect to the vault which remains upright without support, so can the woman who has no husband not enjoy complete happiness. From the words, *It forms a hollow like that of a kettle,* you may judge how lascivious God has made that woman in her comparisons; she likens her vulva to a kettle, which serves to prepare the *tserid*.[174] Listen; if the *tserid* is placed in the kettle, to turn out well it must be stirred by means of a *medeleuk*[175] long and solid, whilst the kettle is steadied by the feet and hands. Only in that way can it be properly prepared. It cannot be done with a small spoon; the cook would burn her hands, owing to the shortness of the handle, and the dish would not be well prepared. This is the symbol of this woman's nature, O Djoâidi. If your member has not the dimensions of a respectable *medeleuk*, serviceable for the good preparation of the *tserid*, it will not give her satisfaction, and, moreover, if you do not hold her close to your chest, enlacing her with your hands and feet, it is useless to solicit her favours; finally if you let her consume herself by her own fire, like the bottom of the kettle which gets burnt if the *medeleuk* is not stirred upon it, you will not gratify her desire by the result.

You see now what prevented her from acceding to your wishes; she was afraid that you would not be able to quench her flame after having fanned it.

'But what is the name of this woman, O Djoâidi?'

'Fadehat el Djemal (the sunrise of beauty),' I replied.

'Return to her,' said the sage, 'and take her these verses, and your affair will come to a happy issue, please God! You will then come back to me, and inform me of what will have come to pass between you two.'

---

[174] The *tserid*, or more commonly *tserida*, is an Arabian dish.

[175] Note in the autograph edition: *Medeleuk*, from *deleuk*, to pound, mash. This is a large wooden spoon, corresponding in shape and size to a pouch. This latter expression, however, being vulgar, has not been employed.

I gave my promise, and Abou Nouass recited to me the following lines:

> Have patience now, O Fadehat el Djemal,
> I understand your words, and all shall see how I obey them.
> O you! beloved and cherished by whoever
> Can revel in your charms and glory in them!
> O apple of my eye! You thought I was embarrassed
> About the answer which I had to give you.
> Yes, certainly! It was the love I bore you
> Made me look foolish in the eyes of all you know.
> They thought I was possessed of a demon;
> Called me a Merry Andrew and buffoon.
> For God! What of buffoonery I've got,
>   Should it be that
> No other member is like mine? Here! see it, measure it!
> What woman tastes it falls in love with me,
> In violent love. It is a well known fact
> That you from far may see it like a column.
> If it erects itself it lifts my robe and shames me.
> Now take it kindly, put it in your tent,
> Which is between the well known mountains placed.
> It will be quite at home there, you will find it
> Not softening while inside, but sticking like a nail;
> Take it to form a handle to your vase.
> Come and examine it, and notice well
> How vigorous it is and long in its erection!
> If you but want a proper *medeleuk*,
> A *medeleuk* to use between your thighs,
> Take this to stir the centre of your kettle.
> It will do good to you, O mistress mine!
> Your kettle be it plated will be satisfied![176]

Having learnt these verses by heart, I took my leave of Abou Nouass and returned to Fadehat el Djemal. She was, as usual, alone. I gave a slight knock at her door; she came out at once, beautiful as the rising sun, and coming up to me, she said, 'Oh! enemy of God, what business has brought you here to me at this time?'

I answered her, 'O my mistress! a business of great importance.'

---

[176] Note in the autograph edition: The Arabs have a vulgar saying, regarding a man who is not easily satisfied, that he is *mokeus deur*, plated. Doubtless it refers in a similar sense to the vulva.

'Explain yourself, and I will see whether I can help you,' she said.

'I shall not speak to you about it until the door is locked,' I answered.

'Your boldness today is very great,' she said.

And I, 'True, O my mistress! boldness is one of my qualities.'

She then addressed me thus, 'O enemy of yourself! O you most miserable of your race! If I were to lock the door, and you have nothing wherewith to satisfy my desires, what should I do with you? face of a Jew!'

'You will let me share your couch, and grant me your favours.'

She began to laugh; and after we had entered the house, she told a slave to lock the house door. As usual, I asked her to respond to my proposals; she then recited to me again the above mentioned verses. When she had finished I began to recite to her those which Abou Nouass had taught me.

As I proceeded I saw her more and more moved, I observed her giving way, to yawn, to stretch herself, to sigh. I knew now I should arrive at the desired result. When I had finished my member was in such a state of erection that it became like a pillar, still lengthening. When Fadehat el Djemal saw it in that condition she precipitated herself upon it, took it into her hands, and drew it towards her thighs. I then said, 'O apple of my eyes! this may not be done here, let us go into your chamber.'

She replied, 'Leave me alone, O son of a debauched woman! Before God! I am losing my senses in seeing your member getting longer and longer, and lifting your robe. Oh, what a member! I never saw a finer one! Let it penetrate into this delicious, plump vulva, which maddens all who heard it described; for the sake of which so many died of love; and of which your superiors and masters themselves could not get possession.'

I repeated, 'I shall not do it anywhere else than in your chamber.'

She answered, 'If you do not enter this minute this tender vulva I shall die.'

As I still insisted upon repairing to her room, she cried, 'No, it is quite impossible; I cannot wait so long!'

I saw in fact her lips tremble, her eyes filling with tears. A general tremor ran over her, she changed colour, and laid herself down upon her back, baring her thighs, the whiteness of which made her flesh appear like crystal tinged with carmine.

Then I examined her vulva – a white cupola with a purple centre, soft and charming. It opened like that of a mare on the approach of a stallion.

At that moment she seized my member and kissed it, saying, 'By the religion of my father! it must penetrate into my vulva!' and drawing nearer to me she pulled it towards her vagina.

I now hesitated no longer to assist her with my member, and placed it against the entrance to her vulva. As soon as the head of my member touched the lips, the whole body of Fadehat el Djemal trembled with excitement. Sighing and sobbing, she held me pressed to her bosom.

Again I profited by this moment to admire the beauties of her vulva. It was magnificent, its purple centre setting off its whiteness all the more. It was round, and without any imperfection; projecting like a splendidly curved dome over her belly. In one word, it was a masterpiece of creation as fine as could be seen. The blessing of God, the best creator, upon it.

And the woman who possessed this wonder had in her time no superior.

Seeing her then in such transports, trembling like a bird, the throat of which is being cut, I pushed my dart into her. But thinking she might not be able to take in the whole of my member, I had entered cautiously, but she moved her buttocks furiously, saying to me, 'This is not enough for my contentment.' Making a strong push, I lodged my member completely in her, which made her utter a painful cry, but the moment after she moved with greater fury than before. She cried, 'Do not miss the corners, neither high nor low, but above all things do not neglect the centre! The centre!' she repeated. 'If you feel it

coming, let it go into my matrix so as to extinguish my fire.'
Then we moved alternately in and out, which was delicious. Our
legs were interlaced, our muscles unbent, and so we went on with
kisses and claspings until the crisis came upon us simultaneously.
We then rested and took breath after this mutual conflict.

I wanted to with-draw my member, but she would not consent
to this and begged of me not to take it out. I acceded to her wish,
but a moment later she took it out herself, dried it, and replaced
it in her vulva. We renewed our game, kissing, pressing, and
moving in rhythm. After a short time, we rose and entered her
chamber, without having this time accomplished the enjoyment.
She gave me now a piece of an aromatic root,[177] which she recommended me to keep in my mouth, assuring me that as long as I
had it there my member would remain on the alert. Then she
asked me to lie down, which I did. She mounted upon me, and
taking my member into her hands, she made it enter entirely
into her vagina. I was astonished at the vigour of her vulva and
at the heat emitted from it. The opening of her matrix in
particular excited my admiration. I never had any experience like
it; it closely clasped my member and pinched the gland.

With the exception of Fadehat el Djemal no woman had until
then taken in my member to its full length. She was able to do
so, I believe, owing to her being very plump and corpulent, and
her vulva being large and deep.

Fadehat el Djemal, astride upon me, began to rise and descend;
she kept crying out, wept, went slower, then accelerated her
movements again, ceased to move altogether; when part of my
member became visible she looked at it, then took it out
altogether to examine it closely, then plunged it in again until
it had disappeared completely. So she continued until the
enjoyment overcame her again. At last, having dismounted from
me, she now laid herself down, and asked me to get on to her. I
did so, and she introduced my member entirely into her vulva.

We thus continued our caresses, changing our positions in

[177] Probably cinnamon or the root of the cubeb-plant.

turns, until night came on. I thought it proper to show a wish to go now, but she would not agree to this, and I had to give her my word that I would remain. I said to myself, 'This woman will not let me go at any price, but when daylight comes God will advise me.' I remained with her, and all night long we kept caressing each other, and took but scanty rest.

I counted that during that day and night, I accomplished twenty-seven times the act of coition, and I became afraid that I should nevermore be able to leave the house of that woman.

Having at last made good my escape, I went to visit Abou Nouass again, and informed him of all that had happened. He was surprised and stupefied, and his first words were, 'O Djoâidi, you can have neither authority nor power over such a woman, and she would make you do penance for all the pleasure you have had with other women!'

However, Fadehat el Djemal proposed to me to become her legitimate husband, in order to put a stop to the vexatious rumours that were circulating about her conduct. I, on the other hand, was only on the look out for adultery. Asking the advice of Abou Nouass about it, he told me, 'If you marry Fadehat el Djemal you will ruin your health, and God will with-draw his protection[178] from you, and the worst of all will be that she will cuckold you, for she is insatiable with respect to the coitus, and would cover you with shame.' And I answered him, 'Such is the nature of women; they are insatiable as far as their vulvas are concerned, and so long as their lust is satisfied they do not care whether it be with a buffoon, a negro, a valet, or even with a man that is despised and reprobated by society.'

On this occasion Abou Nouass depicted the character of women in the following verses:

> Women are demons, and were born as such;
> No one can trust them, as is known to all;
> If they love a man, it is only out of caprice;

[178] The Arab word *seteur* signifies veil, window-blind, and by extension, protection or even shield, buckler. It was in this latter sense that the author has used the word here.

And he to whom they are most cruel loves them most.
Beings full of treachery and trickery, I aver
The man that loves you truly is a lost man;
He who believes me not can prove my word
By letting woman's love get hold of him for years !
If in your own generous mood you have given them
Your all and everything for years and years,
They will say afterwards, 'I swear by God ! my eyes
Have never seen a thing he gave me !'
After you have impoverished yourself for their sake,
Their cry from day to day will be for ever 'Give !
Give man, Get up and buy and borrow.'[179]
If they cannot profit by you they'll turn against you;
They will tell lies about you and calumniate you.
They do not recoil to use a slave in the master's absence,
If once their passions are aroused, and they play tricks;
Assuredly, if once their vulva is in rut,
They only think of getting in some member in erection.
Preserve us, God ! from woman's trickery;
And of old women in particular. So be it.

[179] Note in the autograph edition: Literally: 'Seized by your bounty,' a form of speech used to express the attentions which men show to women.

CHAPTER X

Concerning the Organs of Generation
of Animals

K NOW, O VIZIR (God's blessing be with you!), that the sexual organs of the various male animals are not analogous with the different natures of the virile members which I have mentioned.

The verges of animals are classed according to the species to which they belong, and these species are four in number.

1. The verges of animals with hoofs, as the horse, mule, ass, which verges are of large size.[180]

> *El rermoul,* the colossus.
> *El kass,*[181] the serpent rolled up.
> *El fellag,*[182] the splitter.
> *El zellate,* the club.
> *El heurmak,* the indomitable.
> *El meunefoukh,* the swollen.
> *Abou dommar,* the one with a head.
> *Abou beurnita,* the one with a hat.
> *El keurkite,*[183] the pointed staff.

[180] Note of the autograph edition: Literally, magnificent creation.

[181] The word *kass,* from the root *kass,* means to pierce a female; in coitus, enwrapping her like a serpent.

[182] This name comes from the root *felleg,* to split, to divide in two.

[183] *Keurkite* is the name of a staff with a long, pointed ferrule, as carried by the Marabouts. In some texts this name is replaced by *keurnite,* the Arabian name for lobster, and also for a sort of cuttle fish abounding on the African coast.

El *keuntra*, the bridge.
El *rezama*, the mallet.
Abou *sella*, the fighter.[184]

2. The verges of animals which have the kind of feet called *akhefaf*,[185] as, for instance, the camel.

El *mâloum*, the well-known.
El *tonil*, the long one.
El *cherita*, the riband.[186]
El *mostakime*, the firm one.
El *heurkal*, the swinging one.
El *mokheubbi*, the hidden one.
El *châaf*, the tuft.[187]
Tsequil *el ifaha*, the slow-coach.

3. The verges of animals with split hoofs, like the ox, the sheep, etc.

El *aceub*, the nerve.
El *heurbadj*, the rod.
El *sonte*, the whip.
Requig *er ras*, the small head.
El *tonil*, the long one.

For the ram.
El *aïçoub*, the nervous.

And lastly, the members of animals with claws, as the lion, fox, dog, and other animals of this species.

El *kedib*, the verge.
El *kibouss*, the great gland.
El *metemerole*, the one that will lengthen.

[184] See note 151 on page 180.
[185] Note in the autograph edition: *Akhefaf* has no equivalent in French. It is a foot showing rudimentary hoofs or toes united at the sole by a thick and callous epidermis, as seen in the camel.
[186] *Id. Cherita* means a plaited riband or flat cord.
[187] *Id.* The only sense which can be found in châaf is that of tuft, frieze, hair in general.

It is believed that of all the animals of God's creation the lion is the most expert in respect to coition. If he meets the lioness he examines her before copulation. He will know if she has already been covered by a male. When she comes to him he smells at her, and if she has allowed herself to be crossed by a boar he knows it immediately by the odour that animal has left upon her. He then smells her urine, and if the examination proves unfavourable, he gets into a rage, and begins to lash with his tail right and left. Woe to the animal that comes at that time near him; it is certain to be torn to pieces. He then returns to the lioness, who, seeing that he knows all, trembles with terror. He smells again at her, utters a roar which makes the mountains shake, and, falling upon her, lacerates her back with his claws. He even will go so far as to kill her, and then befoul her body with his urine.

It is said that the lion is the most jealous and most intelligent of all animals. It is also averred that he is generous, and spares him who gets round him by fair words.

A man who on meeting a lion uncovers his sexual parts causes him to take to flight.

Whoever pronounces before a lion the name of Daniel (Hail be to him!),[188] also sends him flying, because the prophet (Hail be to him!) has enjoined this upon the lion in respect to the invocation of his name. Therefore, when this name is pronounced, the lion departs without doing any harm. Several cases which prove this fact are cited.

[188] It is probable that this belief originates with the sojourn of Daniel in the lions' den.

CHAPTER XI

On the Deceits and Treacheries of Women

K NOW, O VIZIR (to whom God be good!) that the stratagems of women are numerous and ingenious. Their tricks
will deceive Satan himself, for God, the Highest has said
(Koran, chapter xii., verse 28), that the deceptive faculties of
women are great, and he has likewise said (Koran, chapter vi.,
verse 38), that the stratagems of Satan are weak. Comparing the
word of God as to the ruses of Satan and woman, contained in
those two verses, it is easy to see how great these latter ones
are.[189]

Story of a Deceived Husband being Convicted Him-
self of Infidelity

It is related that a man fell in love with a woman of great
beauty, and possessing all perfections imaginable. He had made
many advances to her, which were repulsed; then he had
endeavoured to seduce her by rich presents, which were likewise
declined. He lamented, complained, and was prodigal with his
money in order to conquer her, but to no purpose, and he grew
lean as a spectre.

This lasted for some time, when he made the acquaintance
of an old woman, whom he took into his confidence, complaining
bitterly about it. She said to him, 'I shall help you, please God.'

Forthwith she made her way to the house of the woman, in

[189] 'The nature of woman is such.' (*Rabelais*, book iii, chap. 33.)

order to get an interview with her; but on arriving there the neighbours told her that she could not get in, because the house was guarded by a ferocious bitch, which did not allow anyone to come in or to depart, and in her malignity always flew at the faces of people.

Hearing this, the old woman rejoiced, and said to herself, 'I shall succeed, please God.' She then went home, and filled a basket with bits of meat. Thus provided, she returned to the woman's house, and went in.

The bitch, on seeing her, rose to spring at her; but she produced the basket with its contents, and showed it her. As soon as the brute saw the viands, it showed its satisfaction by the movements of its tail and nostrils. The old woman putting down the basket before it, spoke to it as follows, 'Eat, O my sister. Your absence has been painful to me; I did not know what had become of you, and I have been looking for you a long time. Appease your hunger!'

While the animal was eating, and she stroked its back, the mistress of the house came to see who was there, and was not a little surprised to see the bitch, which would never suffer anybody to come near her, so friendly with a strange person. She said, 'O old woman, how is it that you know our dog?' The old woman gave no reply, but continued to caress the animal, and utter lamentations.

Then said the mistress of the house to her, 'My heart aches to see you thus. Tell me the cause of your sorrow.'

'This bitch,' said the woman, 'was formerly a woman, and my best friend. One fine day she was invited with me to a wedding; she put on her best clothes, and adorned herself with her finest ornaments. We then went together. On our way we were accosted by a man, who at her sight was seized with the most violent love; but she would not listen to him. Then he offered brilliant presents, which she also declined. This man, meeting her some days later, said to her, "Surrender yourself to my passion, or else I shall conjure God to change you into a bitch." She answered,

o

"Conjure as much as you like." The man then called the maledictions of heaven upon that woman, and she was changed into a bitch, as you see here.'

At these words the mistress of the house began to cry and lament, saying, 'O, my mother! I am afraid that I shall meet the same fate as this bitch.' 'Why, what have you done?' said the old woman. The other answered, 'There is a man who has loved me since a long time, and I have refused to accede to his desires, nor did I listen to him, though the saliva was dried up in his mouth by his supplications; and in spite of the large expenses he had gone to in order to gain my favour I have always answered him that I should not consent, and now, O my mother, I am afraid that he might call to God to curse me.'

'Tell me how to know this man,' said the old woman, 'for fear that you might become like this animal.'

'But how will you be able to find him, and whom could I send to him?'

The old woman answered, 'Me, daughter of mine! I shall render you this service, and find him.'

'Make haste, O my mother, and see him before he conjures God against me.'

'I shall find him still this day,' answered the old woman, 'and, please God, you shall meet him tomorrow.'

With this, the old woman took her leave, went on the same day to the man who had made her his confidant, and told him of the meeting arranged for next day.

So the next day the mistress of the house went to the old woman, for they had agreed that the rendezvous should take place there. When she arrived at the house she waited for some time, but the lover did not come. No doubt he had been prevented from making his appearance by some matter of importance.

The old woman, reflecting upon this mischance, thought to herself, 'There is no might nor power but in God, the Great. But she could not imagine what might have kept him away. Looking at the woman, she saw that she was agitated, and it was apparant that she wanted coition hotly. She got more and more restless, and presently asked, 'Why does he not come?' The old woman made answer, 'O my daughter, some serious affair must have interfered, probably necessitating a journey. But I shall help you under these circumstances.' She then put on her *melahfa*,[190] and went to look for the young man. But it was to no purpose, as she could not find out anything about him.

Still continuing her search, the old woman was thinking, 'This woman is at this moment eagerly coveting a man. Why not try today another young man, who might calm her ardour? Tomorrow I shall find the right one.' As she was thus walking and thinking she met a young man of very pleasing exterior. She saw, at once, that he was a fit lover, and likely to help her out of her perplexity; and she spoke to him: 'O my son, if I were to set you in connection with a lady, beautiful, graceful and perfect, would you make love to her?' 'If your words are truth, I would give you this golden dinar!' said he. The old woman, quite enchanted, took the money, and conducted him to her house.

Now, it so happened that this young man was the husband of the lady, which the old woman did not know till she had brought him. And the way she found it out was this: She went first into the house and said to the lady, 'I have not been able to find the slightest trace of your lover; but, failing him, I have brought you somebody to quench your fire for today. We will save the other for tomorrow. God has inspired me to do so.'

The lady then went to the window to take a look at him whom the old woman wanted to bring to her, and, getting sight of him, she recognized her husband, just on the point of entering the house.[191] She did not hesitate, but hastily donning her *melahfa*,

[190] The *melahfa* is a large veil, generally of white cotton web, used by women to wrap themselves in, both body and head, when they walk out.
[191] Note in the autograph edition: An analogous situation is found in the *Tales of Boccaccio*, Tale Six of the Third Day, done into verse by La Fontaine, in the story of Richard Minutolo (*First Book of the Tales*). It must be added that the groundwork of the Arabian tale is different from Boccaccio's. Observe, however, that the means employed by the old woman to gain for the young man the lady's favours is not without analogy to those described in Tale Eight of the Fifth Day of the same book.

she went straight to meet him, and striking him in the face, she exclaimed, 'O! enemy of God and of yourself, what are you doing here? You surely came with the intention to commit adultery. I have been suspecting you for a long time, and waited here every day, while I was sending out the old woman to inveigle you to come in. This day I have found you out, and denial is of no use. And you always told me that you were not a rake! I shall demand a divorce this very day, now I know your conduct!'

The husband, believing that his wife spoke the truth, remained silent and abashed.

Learn from this the deceitfulness of woman, and what she is capable of.

Story of the Lover against his Will

A story is told of a certain woman who was desperately in love with one of her neighbours, whose virtue and piety were well known. She declared to him her passion; but, finding all her advances constantly repulsed, in spite of all her wiles, she resolved to have her satisfaction nevertheless, and this is the way she went to work her purpose:

One evening she apprised her negress that she intended to set a snare for that man, and the negress, by her order, left the street door open; then, in the middle of the night, she called the negress and gave her the following instructions: 'Go and knock with this stone at our street door as hard as you can, without taking any notice of the cries which I shall utter, or the noise I make; as soon as you hear the neighbour opening his door, come back and knock the same way at the inner door.[192] Take care that he does not see you, and come in at once if you observe somebody coming.' The negress executed this order punctually.

Now, the neighbour was by nature a compassionate man, always disposed to assist people in distress, and his help was

[192] Note in the autograph edition: Arabian houses are generally situated in an inner court, which communicates by a door with the street, while a second door leads to the appartments.

never asked in vain. On hearing the noise of the blows struck at the door and the cries of his neighbour, he asked his wife what this might mean, and she replied, 'It is our neighbour so and so, who is attacked in her house by thieves.' He went in great haste to her aid; but scarcely had he entered the house when the negress closed the door upon him. The woman seized him, and uttered loud screams. He protested, but the mistress of the house put, without any more ado, this condition before him. 'If you do not consent to do with me so and so, I shall tell that you have come in here to violate me, and hence all this noise.' 'The will of God be done!' said the man, 'nobody can go against Him, nor escape from His might.' He then tried sundry subterfuges in order to escape, but in vain, for the mistress of the house recommenced to scream and make a row, which brought a good many people to the spot. He saw that his reputation would be compromised if he continued his resistance, and surrendered, saying, 'Save me, and I am ready to satisfy you!' 'Go into this chamber and close the door behind you,' said the lady of the house, 'if you want to leave this house with honour, and do not attempt escape unless you wish those people to know that you are the author of all this commotion.' When he saw how determined she was to have her way, he did as she had told him. She, on her part, went out to the neighbours that had come to help her, and giving them some kind of explanation, dismissed them. They went away condoling with her.

Left alone, she shut the doors and returned to her unwilling lover. She kept him in sequestration for a whole week, and only set him free after she had completely drained him.

Learn from this the deceitfulness of women, and what they are capable of.

A Larceny of Love

The following story is told of two women who inhabited the same house. The husband of one of them had a member long, thick and hard; while the husband of the other had, on the contrary, that organ little, insignificant and soft. The first one rose always pleasant and smiling; the other one got up in the morning in tears and vexation.

One day the two women were together, and spoke of their husbands.

The first one said, 'I live in the greatest happiness. My bed is a couch of bliss. When my husband and I are together in it it is the witness of our supreme pleasure; of our kisses and embraces, of our joys and amorous sighs. When my husband's member is in my vulva it stops it up completely; it stretches itself out until it touches the bottom of my vagina, and it does not take its leave until it has visited every corner – threshold, vestibule, ceiling and centre. When the crisis arrives it takes its position in the very centre of the vagina, which it floods with tears. It is in this way we quench our fire and appease our passion.'

The second answered, 'I live in the greatest grief; our bed is a bed of misery, and our coition is a union of fatigue and trouble, of hate and malediction. When my husband's member enters my vulva there is a space left open, and it is so short it cannot touch the bottom. When it is in erection it is twisted all ways, and cannot procure any pleasure. Feeble and meagre, it can scarcely ejaculate a drop, and its service cannot afford pleasure to any woman.'

Such was the almost daily conversation which the two women had together.

It happened, however, that the woman who had so much cause for complaint thought in her heart how delightful it would be to commit adultery with the other one's husband. She thought to herself, 'It must be brought about, if it be only for once.' Then she watched her opportunity until her husband had to be absent for a night from the house.

In the evening she made preparation to get her project carried out, and perfumed herself with sweet scents and essences. When the night was advanced to about a third of its duration, she noiselessly entered the chamber in which the other woman and her husband were sleeping, and groped her way to their couch. Finding that there was a free space between them, she slipped in. There was scant room, but each of the spouses thought it was the pressure of the other, and gave way a little; and so she contrived to glide between them. She then quietly waited until the other woman was in a profound sleep, and then, approaching the husband, she brought her flesh in contact with his. He awoke, and smelling the perfumed odours which she exhaled, he was in erection at once. He drew her towards him, but she said, in a low voice, 'Let me go to sleep!' He answered, 'Be quiet, and let me do! The children will not hear anything!' She then pressed close up to him, so as to get him farther away from his wife, and said, 'Do as you like, but do not awaken the children, who are close by.' She took these precautions for fear that his wife should wake up.

The man, however, roused by the odour of the perfumes, drew her ardently towards himself. She was plump and mellow, and her vulva projecting. He mounted upon her and said, 'Take it (the member) in your hand, as usual!' She took it, and was astonished at its size and magnificence, then introduced it into her vulva.

The man, however, observed that his member had been taken in entirely, which he had never been able to do with his wife. The woman, on her part, found that she had never received such a benefit from her husband.

The man was quite surprised. He worked his will upon her a second and third time, but his astonishment only increased. At last her got off her, and stretched himself along her side.

As soon as the woman found that he was asleep, she slipped out, left the chamber, and returned to her own.

In the morning, the husband, on rising, said to his wife, 'Your embraces have never seemed so sweet to me as last night, and I never breathed such sweet perfumes as those you exhaled.' 'What embraces and what perfumes are you speaking of?' asked the wife. 'I have not a particle of perfume in the house.' She called him a storyteller, and assured him that he must have been dreaming. He then began to consider whether he might not have deceived himself, and agreed with his wife that he must actually have dreamed it all.

Appreciate, after this, the deceitfulness of women, and what they are capable of.

Story of the Woman with Two Husbands

It is related that a man, after having lived for some time in a country to which he had gone, became desirous of getting married. He addressed himself to an old woman who had experience in such matters, asking her whether she could find him a wife, and who replied, 'I can find you a girl gifted with great beauty, and perfect in shape and comeliness. She will surely suit you, for, besides, having these qualities, she is virtuous and pure. Only mark, her business occupies her all the day, but during the night she will be yours completely. It is for this reason she keeps herself reserved, as she apprehends that a husband might not agree to this.'

The man replied, 'This girl need not be afraid. I, too, am not at liberty during the day, and I only want her for the night.'

He then asked her in marriage. The old woman brought her to him, and he liked her. From that time they lived together, observing the conditions under which they had come together.

This man had an intimate friend whom he introduced to the old woman who had arranged his marriage according to the conditions mentioned, and which friend had requested the man to ask her to do him the same service. They went to the old woman and solicited her assistance in the matter. 'This is a very easy matter,' she said. 'I know a girl of great beauty, who will dissipate your heaviest troubles. Only the business she is carrying on keeps her at work all night, but she will be with your friend all day long.' 'This shall be no hindrance,' replied the friend. She then brought the young girl to him. He was well pleased with her, and married her on the conditions agreed upon.

But before long the two friends found out that the two wives which the old harridan had procured for them were only one woman.

Appreciate, after this, the deceitfulness of women, and what they are capable of.

Story of Bahia

It is related that a married woman of the name of Bahia (splendid beauty) had a lover whose relations to her were soon a mystery to no one, for which reason she had to leave him. Her absence affected him to such a degree that he fell ill, because he could not see her.

One day he went to see one of his friends, and said to him, 'Oh, my brother! an ungovernable desire has seized me, and I can wait no more. Could you accompany me on a visit I am going to pay to Bahia, the well-beloved of my heart?' The friend declared himself willing.

The next day they mounted their horses; and after a journey of two days, they arrived near the place where Bahia dwelt. There they stopped. The lover said to his friend, 'Go and see the people that live about here, and ask for their hospitality, but take good care not to divulge our intentions, and try in particular to find the servant-girl of Bahia, to whom you can say that I am here, and whom you will charge with the message to her mistress that I would like to see her.' He then described the servant-maid to him.

The friend went, met the servant, and told her all that was necessary. She went at once to Bahia, and repeated to her what she had been told.

Bahia sent to the friend the message, 'Inform him who sent you that the meeting will take place tonight, near such and such a tree, at such and such an hour.'

Returning to the lover, the friend communicated to him the decision of Bahia about the rendezvous.

At the hour that had been fixed, the two friends were near to the tree. They had not to wait long for Bahia. As soon as her lover saw her coming, he rushed to meet her, kissed her, pressed her to his heart, and they began to embrace and caress each other.

The lover said to her, 'O Bahia, is there no way to enable us to pass the night together without rousing the suspicions of your husband?' She answered, 'Oh, before God! if it will give you pleasure, the means to contrive this are not wanting.' 'Hasten,' said her lover, 'to let me know how it may be done.' She then asked him, 'Your friend here, is he devoted to you, and intelligent?' He answered, 'Yes.' She then rose, took off her garments, and handed them to the friend, who gave her his, in which she then dressed herself; then she made the friend put on her clothes. The lover said, surprised, 'What are you going to do?' 'Be silent,' she answered, and addressing herself to the friend, she gave him the following explanations: 'Go to my house and lie down in my bed. After a third part of the night is passed, my husband will come to you and ask you for the pot into which they milk the camels. You will then take up the vase, but you must keep it in your hands until he takes it from you. This is our usual way. Then he will go and return with the pot filled with milk, and say to you, "Here is the pot!" But you must not take it from him until he has repeated these words. Then take it out of his hands, or let him put it on the ground himself. After that, you will not see anything more of him till the morning. After the pot has been put on the ground, and my husband is gone, drink the third part of the milk, and replace the pot on the ground.'

The friend went, observed all these recommendations, and when the husband returned with the pot full of milk he did not take it out of his hands until he had said twice, 'Here is the pot!' Unfortunately he with-drew his hands when the husband was going to set it down, the latter thinking the pot was being held, let it go, and the vase fell upon the ground and was broken. The husband, in the belief that he was speaking to his wife, exclaimed, 'What have you been thinking of?' and beat him with it till it broke; then took another, and continued to batter him stroke on stroke enough to break his back. The mother and sister of Bahia came running to the spot to tear her from his hands. He had fainted. Luckily they succeeded in getting the husband away.

The mother of Bahia soon came back, and talked to him so long that he was fairly sick of her talk; but he could do nothing but be silent and weep. At last she finished, saying, 'Have confidence in God, and obey your husband. As for your lover, he cannot come now to see and console you, but I will send your sister to keep you company.' And so she went away.

She did send, indeed, the sister of Bahia, who began to console her and curse him who had beaten her. He felt his heart warming towards her, for he had seen that she was of resplendent beauty, endowed with all perfections, and like the full moon in the night. He placed his hand over her mouth, so as to prevent her from speaking, and said to her, 'O, lady! I am not what you think. Your sister Bahia is at present with her lover, and I have run into danger to do her a service. Will you not take me under your protection? If you denounce me, your sister will be covered with shame; as for me, I have done my part, but may the evil fall back upon you!'

The young girl then began to tremble like a leaf, in thinking of the consequences of her sister's doings, and then beginning to laugh, surrendered herself to the friend who proved himself so true. They passed the remainder of the night in bliss, kisses, embraces, and mutual enjoyment. He found her the best of the best. In her arms he forgot the beating he had received, and they did not cease to play, toy, and make love till daybreak.

He then returned to his companion. Bahia asked him how he had fared, and he said to her, 'Ask your sister. By my faith! she knows it all! Only know, that we have passed the night in mutual pleasures, kissing and enjoying ourselves until now.'

Then they changed clothes again, each one taking his own, and the friend told Bahia all the particulars of what had happened to him.

Appreciate, after this, the deceitfulness of women, and what they are capable of.

The Story of the Man who was an Expert in Stratagems, and was Duped by a Woman

A story is told of a man who had studied all the ruses and all the stratagems invented by women for the deception of men, and pretended that no woman could dupe him.

A woman of great beauty, and full of charms, got to hear of his conceit. She, therefore, prepared for him in the *medjélés*[193] a collation, in which several kinds of wine figured, and nothing was wanting in the way of rare and choice viands. Then she sent for him, and invited him to come and see her. As she was famed for her great beauty and the rare perfection of her person, she had roused his desires, and he made haste to avail himself of her invitation.

She was dressed in her finest garments, and exhaled the choicest perfumes, and assuredly whoever had thus seen her would have been troubled in his mind. And thus, when he was admitted into her presence, he was fascinated by her charms, and plunged into admiration by her marvellous beauty.

This woman, however, appeared to be preoccupied on account of her husband, and allowed it to be seen that she was afraid of his coming back from one minute to another. It must be mentioned that this husband was very proud, very jealous, and very violent, and would not have hesitated to shed the blood of anyone whom he would have found prowling about his house.

[193] The *medjélés*, from *djéleuss*, to sit down, is the name of a saloon in Arab houses, generally situated on the ground floor. It is the vestibule, the saloon for visitors.

What would he have done, and, with much more reason, to the
man whom he might have found inside !

While the lady and he, who flattered himself that he should
possess her, were amusing themselves in the *medjélés*, a knock
at the house-door filled the lover with fear and trouble, particularly when the lady cried, 'This is my husband, who is returning.' All in a tremble, she hid him in a closet, which was in the
room, shut the door upon him, and left the key in the *medjélés;*
then she opened the house-door.

Her husband, for it was he, saw, on entering, the wine and all
the preparations that had been made. Surprised, he asked what
this meant. 'It means what you see,' she answered. 'But for
whom is all this?' he asked.

'It is for my lover whom I have here.'

'And where is he?'

'In this closet,' she said, pointing with her finger to the place
where the sufferer was confined.

At these words the husband started. He rose and went to the
closet, but found it locked. 'Where is the key?' he said. She
answered, 'Here!' throwing it to him. But as he was putting it
into the lock she burst out laughing uproariously. He turned
towards her, and said, 'What are you laughing at?' 'I laugh,'
she answered, 'at the weakness of your judgment, and your want
of reason and reflection. Oh, you man without sense, do you
think that if I had in reality a lover, and had admitted him into
this room, I should have told you that he was here and where he
was hidden? That is certainly not likely. I had no other thought
than to offer you a collation on your return, and wanted only
to have a joke with you in doing as I did. If I had had a lover I
should certainly not have made you my confidant.'

The husband left the key in the lock of the closet without
having turned it, returned to the table, and said, 'True! I rose;
but I have not the slightest doubt about the sincerity of your
words.' Then they ate and drank together, and made love.

The man in the closet had to stop there until the husband

went out. Then the lady went to set him free, and found him quite undone and in a bad state. When he came out, after having escaped an eminent peril, she said to him, 'Well, you wiseacre, who know so well the stratagems of women, of all those you know, is there one to equal this?' He made answer, 'I am now convinced that your stratagems are countless.'

Appreciate after this the deceits of women, and what they are capable of.

Story of the Lover who was surprised by the Unexpected Arrival of the Husband

It is related that a woman who was married to a violent and brutal man, having her lover with her on the unexpected arrival of her husband, who was returning from a journey, had only just time to hide him under the bed. She was compelled to let him remain in this dangerous and unpleasant position, knowing of no expedient which might enable him to leave the house. In her restlessness she went to and fro, and having gone to the street-door, one of her neighbours, a woman, saw that she was in trouble, and asked her the reason of it. She told her what had happened. The other one then said, 'Return into the house. I will charge myself with the safety of your lover, and I promise you that he shall come out unharmed.' Then the woman re-entered her house.

Her neighbour was not long in joining her, and together they prepared the meal, and then they all sat down to eat and drink. The woman sat facing her husband, and the neighbour opposite the bed. The latter began to tell stories and anecdotes about the tricks of women; and the lover under the bed heard all that was going on.

Pursuing her tales, the neighbour told the following one: 'A married woman had a lover, whom she loved tenderly, and by whom she was equally loved. One day the lover came to see her in the absence of her husband. But the latter happened to return home unexpectedly just as they were together. The woman, knowing of no better place, hid her lover under the bed, then sat down by her husband, who was taking some refreshment, and joked and played with him. Amongst other playful games, she covered her husband's eyes with a napkin, and her lover took this opportunity to come out from under the bed and escape unobserved.'

The wife understood at once how to profit by this tale; taking a napkin and covering the eyes of her husband with it, she said, 'Then it was by means of this ruse that the lover was helped out of his dilemma.' And the lover, taking the opportunity, succeeded in making good his escape unobserved by the husband. Unconscious of what had happened this latter laughed at the story, and his merriment was still increased by the last words of his wife and by her action.

Appreciate after this the deceitfulness of women, and what they are capable of.

CHAPTER XII

Concerning Sundry Observations useful to know for Men and Women

KNOW, O VIZIR (to whom God be good!), that the information contained in this chapter is of the greatest utility,
and it is only in this book that such can be found. Assuredly
to know things is better than to be ignorant of them. Knowledge
may be bad, but ignorance is still more so.

The knowledge in question concerns matters unknown to you,
and relating to women.

There was once a woman, named Moârbeda, who was considered to be the most knowing and wisest person of her time.
She was a philosopher. One day various queries were put to her,
and among them the following, which I shall give here, with her
answers.

'In what part of a woman's body does her mind reside?'

'Between her thighs.'

'And where her enjoyment?'

'In the same place.'

'And where the love of men and the hatred of them?'

'In the vulva,' she said; adding, 'to the man whom we love
we give our vulva, and we refuse it to him we hate. We share
our property with the man we love, and are content with whatever little he may be able to bring to us; if he has no fortune, we
take him as he is. But, on the other hand, we keep at a distance
him whom we hate, were he to offer us wealth and riches.'

'Where, in a woman, are located knowledge, love and taste?'
'In the eye, the heart, and the vulva.'

When asked for explanations on this subject, she replied: 'Knowledge dwells in the eye, for it is the woman's eye that appreciates the beauty of form and of appearance. By the medium of this organ love penetrates into the heart and dwells in it, and enslaves it. A woman in love pursues the object of her love, and lays snares for it. If she succeed, there will be an encounter between the beloved one and her vulva. The vulva tastes him and then knows his sweet or bitter flavour. It is, in fact, the vulva which knows how to distinguish by tasting the good from the bad.'

'Which virile members are preferred by women? What women are most eager for coitus, and which are those who detest it? Which are the men preferred by women, and which are those whom they abominate?'

She answered, 'Not all women have the same conformation of vulva, and they also differ in their manner of making love, and in their love for and their aversion to things. The same disparities exist in men, both with regard to their organs and their tastes. A woman of plump form and with a shallow uterus will look out for a member which is both short and thick, which will completely fill her vagina, without touching the bottom of it; a long and large member would not suit her. A woman with a deep lying uterus, and consequently a long vagina, only yearns for a member which is long and thick and of ample proportions, and thus fills her vagina in its whole extension; she will despise the man with a small and slender member for he could never satisfy her in coition.

'The following distinctions exist in the temperaments of women: the bilious, the melancholy, the sanguine, the phlegmatic, and the mixed. Those with a bilious or melancholy temperament are not much given to coitus, and like it only with men of the same disposition. Those who are sanguine or phlegmatic love coition to excess, and if they encounter a member, they would never let it leave their vulva if they could help it. With these also it is only men of their own temperament who can satisfy them, and if such a woman were married to a bilious or melancholy man, they would lead a sorry life together. As regards mixed temperaments, they exhibit neither a marked predilection for, nor aversion against coitus.

'It has been observed that under all circumstances little women love coitus more and evince a stronger affection for the virile member than women of a large size. Only long and vigorous members suit them; in them they find the delight of their existence and of their couch.

'There are also women who love the coitus only on the edge of their vulva, and when a man lying upon them wants to get his member into the vagina, they take it out with the hand and place its gland between the lips of the vulva.'

I have every reason to believe that this is only the case with young girls or with women not used to men. I pray God to preserve us from such, or from women for whom it is a matter of impossibility to give themselves up to men.[194]

'There are women who will do their husband's behests, and will satisfy them and give them voluptuous pleasure by coition, only if compelled by blows and ill-treatment. Some people ascribe this conduct to the aversion they feel either against coition or against the husband; but this is not so; it is simply a question of temperament and character.

'There are also women who do not care for coition because all their ideas turn upon the grandeurs, personal honours, ambitious hopes, or business-cares of the world. With others this indifference springs, as it may be, from purity of the heart, or from jealousy, or from a pronounced tendency of their souls towards another world, or lastly from past violent sorrows. Fur-

---

[194] Note in the autograph edition: This is a parenthesis introduced by the author in the discourse of Moârbeda, giving vent to his indignation. This paragraph, the preceding one, and the two that follow, are not to be found in some of the Arab texts, and on close examination we are convinced that they are interpolated.

thermore, the pleasures which they feel in coition depend not
alone upon the size of the member, but also upon the particular
conformation of their own natural parts. Amongst those the
vulva called from its form *el mortebâ*, the square one, and *el
mortafâ*, the projecting, is remarkable. This vulva has the
peculiarity of projecting all round when the woman is standing
up and closes her thighs. It burns for the coitus, its slit is narrow,
and it is also called *el keulihimi*, the pressed one. The woman
who has such a one likes only large members, and they must
not let her wait long for the crisis. But this is a general characteristic of women.

'As to the desire of men for coition, I must say that they also
are addicted to it more or less according to their different temperaments, five in number,[195] like the women's, with the difference
that the hankering of the woman after the member is stronger
than that of the man after the vulva.'

'What are the faults of women?' Moârbeda replied to this
question, 'The worst of women is she who immediately cries out
aloud as soon as her husband wants to touch the smallest amount
of her property for his necessities. In the same line stands she
who divulges matters which her husband wants to be kept
secret.'

'Are there any more?' she is asked. She adds, 'The woman of
a jealous disposition and the woman who raises her voice so as
to drown that of her husband; she who disseminates scandal; the
woman that scowls; the one who is always burning to let men
see her beauty, and cannot stay at home; and with respect to this
last let me add that a woman who laughs much, and is constantly
seen at the street door, may be taken to be an arrant prostitute.

'Bad also are those women who mind other people's affairs;
those who are always complaining; those who steal things belonging to their husbands; those of a disagreeable and imperious

---

[195] Note in the autograph edition: The text says four, the author, no
doubt, not taking the mixed temperament into account. It has been considered right to make this slight modification in the translation.

temper; those who are not grateful for kindnesses received; those that will not share the conjugal couch, or who incommode their husbands by the uncomfortable positions they take in it; those who are inclined to deceit, treachery, calumny and ruse.

'Then there are still women who are unlucky in whatever they undertake; those who are always inclined to blame and censure; those who invite their husbands to fulfil their conjugal duty only when it is convenient for them; those that make noises in bed; and lastly those who are shameless, without intelligence, tattlers and curious.

'Here you have the worst specimens amongst women.'

CHAPTER XIII

Concerning the Causes of Enjoyment in the Act of Generation

K NOW, O VIZIR (to whom God be good!), that the causes which tend to develop the passion for coition are six in number: the fire of an ardent love, the superabundance of sperm, the proximity of the loved person whose possession is eagerly desired, the beauty of the face, exciting viands, and contact.

Know also, that the causes of the pleasure in cohabitation, and the conditions of enjoyment are numerous, but that the principal and best ones are: the heat of the vulva; the narrowness, dryness, and sweet exhalation of the same. If any one of these conditions is absent, there is at the same time something wanting in the voluptuous enjoyment. But if the vagina unites the required qualifications, the enjoyment is complete. In fact, a moist vulva relaxes the nerves, a cold one robs the member of all its vigour, and bad exhalations from the vagina detract greatly from the pleasure, as is also the case if the latter is very wide.

The acme of enjoyment, which is produced by the abundance and impetuous ejaculation of the sperm, depends upon one circumstance, and this is, that the vulva is furnished with a suction-pump (orifice of the uterus), which will clasp the virile member, and suck up the sperm with an irresistible force. The member once seized by the orifice, the lover is powerless to retain the sperm, for the orifice will not relax its hold until it has extracted every drop of the sperm, and certainly if the crisis arrives before this gripping of the gland takes place, the pleasure of the ejaculation will not be complete.

Know that there are eight things which give strength to and favour the ejaculation. These are: bodily health, the absence of all care and worry, an unembarrassed mind, natural gaiety of spirit, good nourishment, wealth, the variety of the faces of women, and the variety of their complexions.

If you wish to acquire strength for coitus, take fruit of the mastic-tree (*derou*),[196] pound them and macerate them with oil and honey; then drink of the liquid first thing in the morning: you will thus become vigorous for the coitus, and there will be abundance of sperm produced.

The same result will be obtained by rubbing the virile member and the vulva with gall from the jackal. This rubbing stimulates those parts and increases their vigour.

A savant of the name of Djelinouss[197] has said : 'He who feels that he is weak for coition should drink before going to bed a glassful of very thick honey and eat twenty almonds and one hundred grains of the pine tree. He must follow this *régime* for three days. He may also pound onion-seed, sift it and mix it afterwards with honey, stirring the mixture well, and take of this mixture while still fasting.'

A man who would wish to acquire vigour for coition may likewise melt down fat from the hump of a camel, and rub his

[196] The mastic is a tree with many branches, the fruit of which are little red berries, which get black when they ripen. There is an oil extracted from them, which is reputed to have the property of strengthening and hardening the flesh.

[197] Djelinouss was the Arabic name for Galen (*circa* 130-200 A.D.). He was born at Pergamos in Asia Minor, and attained considerable renown as a physician at Rome. For many centuries his works were the standard source of reference for the medical profession. An edition was available in Teubner's Series, 1884-92. His writings were translated into Arabic during the 9th century, and were at once adopted throughout the East. According to one of his Arabic biographers, Abu-'l Faraj, he probably died in Sicily about 201 A.D. He wrote much on philosophical subjects, as well as on medicine. (A.H.W.)

member with it just before the act; it will then perform wonders, and the woman will praise it for its work.

If you would make the enjoyment still more voluptuous, masticate a little cubeb-pepper or cardamom-grains of the large species; put a certain quantity of it upon the head of your member, and then go to work. This will procure for you, as well as for the woman, a matchless enjoyment. The ointment from the balm of Judea or of Mecca[198] produces a similar effect.

If you would make yourself very strong for the coitus, pound very carefully pyrether[199] together with ginger,[200] mix them while pounding with ointment of lilac,[201] then rub with this compound your abdomen, the testicles, and the verge. This will make you ardent for coitus.

You will likewise predispose yourself for cohabitation, sensibly increase the volume of your sperm, gain increased vigour for the action, and procure for yourself extraordinary erections, by eating of chrysocolla[202] the size of a mustard-grain.[203] The excitement resulting from the use of this nostrum is unparalleled, and all your qualifications for coitus will be increased.

[198] Note in the autograph edition: *Amyris gileadensis*, or the Canadian pine.

[199] *Id. Anthemis pyrethrum.*

[200] *Zeundjebil*, the *amomum zingiber*.

[201] The ointment here mentioned is undoubtedly composed of fat (or oil) and lilac leaves, mixed and pounded. These leaves are in fact held to be tonic and astringent, and the capsules produced by the shrub give an extract which serves as a febrifuge.

[202] The chrysocolla is a substance used when soldering metals, and gold in particular, and which in all probability is borax. The word *tinkal*, as the raw borax is called in India, is very like the Arab name *teunkar*. As to the name chrysocolla, it is derived from the Greek.

[203] By the expression of 'the size of a mustard-grain' the Arabs mean a very minute quantity.

Observations in the autograph edition upon the notes [202] and [203]: The translator might easily have been misled by the texts before him, for three texts were found to say, 'by eating chrysocolla and mustard-grain.' This latter substance is exciting enough to seem deserving of recommendation for the purpose.

Several texts have besides instead of *teunkar*, the word *takra*, which is, according to Abd er Rezeug, synonymous with *ferbioune*, and signifies the powdered fruit of *veratrum sabadilla*, a corrosive and dangerous medicine. *Ferbioune* is also used for *inphorbia*.

If you wish the woman to be inspired with a great desire to cohabit with you, take a little of cubebs, pyrether, ginger and cinnamon, which you will have to masticate just before joining her; then moisten your member with your saliva and do her business for her. From that moment she will have such an affection for you that she can scarcely be a moment without you.

The virile member, rubbed with ass's milk, will become uncommonly strong and vigorous.

Green peas, boiled carefully with onions, and powdered with cinnamon, ginger and cardamoms, well pounded, create for the consumer considerable amorous passion and strength in coitus.

CHAPTER XIV

Description of the Uterus of Sterile Women, and Treatment of the Same

KNOW, O VIZIR (God be good to you!), that wise physicians have plunged into this sea of difficulties to very little purpose. Each one has looked at the matter from his own point of view, and in the end the question has been left in the dark.

Amongst the causes which determine the sterility of women may be taken the obstruction in the uterus by clots of blood, the accumulation of water,[204] the want of or defective sperm of the man, organic malformation of the parts of the latter, internal defects in the uterus, stagnation of the courses and the corruption of the menstrual fluid, and the habitual presence of wind in the uterus. Other savants attribute the sterility of women to the action of spirits and spells. Sterility is common in women who are very corpulent, so that their uterus gets compressed and cannot conceive, not being able to take up the sperm, especially if the husband's member is short and his testicles are very fat; in such a case the act of copulation can only be imperfectly completed.

One of the remedies against sterility consists of the marrow from the hump of a camel, which the woman spreads on a piece of linen, and rubs her sexual parts with it, after having been

---

[204] There is reason to believe that the author is speaking here of so-called 'whites,' which occasion protuberances in the genital organs of women.

233

purified subsequently to her courses. To complete the cure, she takes some fruits of the plant called *jackal's grapes*,[205] squeezes the juice out of them into a vase, and then adds a little vinegar; of this medicine she drinks, fasting for seven days, during which time her husband will take care to have copulation with her.

The woman may besides pound a small quantity of sésame-grain and mix its juice with a bean's weight of sandarach[206] powder; of this mixture she drinks during three days after her periods; she is then fit to receive her husband's embraces.

The first of these beverages is to be taken separately, and in the first instance; after this the second, which will have a salutary effect, if so it pleases the Almighty God!

There is still another remedy. A mixture is made of nitre, gall from a sheep or a cow, a small quantity of the plant named *el meusk*,[207] and of the grains of that plant. The woman saturates a plug of soft wool with this mixture, and rubs her vulva with it after menstruation; she then receives the caresses of her husband, and, with the will of God the Highest, will become pregnant.

---

[205] The jackal's-grape, also called fox-grape and *meuknina*, is simply the black nightshade, *solanum nigrum*. This name has been translated erroneously bear's-grape (*uva ursi*), which is nothing else but the arbute tree, which furnishes an anodyne.

[206] Note in the autograph edition: *Sandarach, zemikh el ahmeur*, red arsenic. *Dictionary of Kazimirski*.

[207] The word *meusk* used by the author designates a plant, and signifies also musk. The plant in question is no doubt the tuberose, called in Arabic *meusk el roumi*, the musk of the Christian.

CHAPTER XV

Concerning Medicines which Provoke Abortion

K NOW, O VIZIR (God be good to you!) that the medicines which will bring on abortion, and the ejection of the foetus, are innumerable. But I shall speak of those to you which I have proved, and therefore acknowledge as good, so that everybody may learn what may benefit and what may do harm.

I shall in the first place speak of the madder-root.[208] A small quantity of this substance freshly gathered, or even dried, but in the latter case bruised and moistened at the time when it is to be used, vitiates the virile sperm or kills the foetus, bringing abortion on and provoking menstruation when introduced in the woman's vagina. The same end may be obtained by means of a decoction of the same plant taken fasting by the woman, and used at the same time by an external application to moisten the vagina.

Fumigations with the smoke of burnt cabbage seeds cause abortion, if the woman introduces the vapour into her vagina by means of a tube or reed.

I now come to alum. This substance, powdered, and introduced into the vagina, or sprinkled on the verge before coition, prevents the woman from conceiving by obstructing the arrival of the sperm in the uterus; for it has the property of drying up and contracting the vagina. But the too frequent use of it will

---

[208] Certain texts have *araoua*, which would mean the *buphtalmum silvestram*; but there is reason to believe that it is madder-root which is meant, as according to the work of Abd er Rezeug el Djezairi this is an abortive.

make the woman barren and annihilate all her capability of conception.

The man who at the moment of copulation coats his member with tar,[209] deprives his sperm of its generative faculty. This is the most powerful of all applications, and if a woman during her pregnancy introduces some of the substance repeatedly into her vagina, she will be sterile, and the child will be born dead.

The woman who drinks the weight of a *mitskal* of laurel water, with a little pepper, will cause her courses to flow again, and clear her uterus from the clots of blood which sometimes lodge there. If she makes use of this medicine when she is already pregnant, the embryo will be expelled; and taken after confinement, this medicine has the property of causing the expulsion from the matrix of all deleterious matter and of the after-birth.

The woman who drinks an infusion of coarse cinnamon[210] mixed with red myrrh, and then introduces into her vagina a plug of wool saturated with the mixture, kills the foetus and provokes its expulsion, with the will of God the Highest!

If the foetus dies in the womb, a decoction of yellow wall-flowers in water will cause the expulsion of the same, with the will of God the Highest!

All the above enumerated medicines are efficacious and their effect is certain.[211]

[209] The Arabs have known for a long period the vegetable tar – *guetrane* – and, in fact, the French name for it has been derived from their language. They obtain it by distillation in rough furnaces from the wood of the resinous trees found in their country, the pine and the cedar.

[210] Note in the autograph edition: The common name of cinnamon is *keurfa. Dar sini* is the name of an inferior quality of cinnamon.

[211] One may be permitted to doubt this statement, and some of the instructions seem undesirable, if not *dangerous.* None are at all to be recommended, and it should be impressed upon any uninformed reader that they are to be avoided. (A.H.W.)

CHAPTER XVI

Concerning the Causes of Impotence in Men

K
NOW, O VIZIR (God be good to you!) that there are men
whose sperm is vitiated by the inborn coldness of their
nature, by diseases of their organs,[212] by purulent discharges, and by fevers. There are also men with the urinary canal
in their verge deviating owing to a downward curve; the result
of such conformation is that the seminal liquid cannot be ejected
in a straight direction, but falls downwards.[213]

Other men have the member too short and too small to reach
the neck of the matrix, or their bladder is ulcerated, or they are
affected by other infirmities, which prevent them from coition.

Finally, there are men who arrive quicker at the crisis than
women, in consequence of which the two emissions are not
simultaneous; there is in such cases no conception.[214]

All these circumstances serve to explain the absence of conception in women; but the principal cause of all is the shortness of
the virile member.

As another cause of impotence may be regarded the sudden

[212] Note in the autograph edition: The word *seulss* signifies more particularly the emission of the urine or diabetes; but in the present case it seems
to be applied to genito-urinary maladies in general.

[213] This abnormity is called *hypospadias*. Where, on the contrary, the
opening of the urethra is turned upwards it bears the name of *epispadias*.

[214] Simultaneous orgasm is not at all essential for conception. Nor is a
short penis likely to result in absence of conception. Length or shortness
of the male member has nothing to do with the matter. Nefzawi's remarks
reflect, however, some of the beliefs of the place and period. (A.H.W.)

transmission from hot to cold, and vice versa, and a great number of analogous reasons.

Men whose impotence is due either to the corruption of their sperm owing to their cold nature, or to maladies of the organs, or to discharges or fevers and similar ills, or to their excessive promptness in ejaculation, can be cured. They should eat stimulant pastry containing honey, ginger, pyrether, syrup of vinegar, hellebore, garlic, cinnamon, nut-meg, cardamoms,[215] sparrows' tongues,[216] Chinese cinnamon, long pepper, and other spices. They will be cured by using them.

As to the other afflictions which we have indicated – the curvature of the urethra, the small dimensions of the virile member, ulcers on the bladder, and the other infirmities which are adverse to coition—God only can cure them.

---

[215] Cardamom, already mentioned, is a very aromatic medicinal seed which comes from Italy, and is used in the preparation of theriac. It is the fruit of several kinds of the *amomum* tree, and especially of the *amomum cardamomum*.

[216] Sparrow's tongue, *stallena panerina*, sparrow-wort.
Observation in the autograph edition: We are not of that opinion. The sparrow's tongue, as above, seems to be nothing else than the seed of the ash tree. (See the *Dictionaries of Kazimirski* and *Beaussier*, and the Book on Medicines of Abd er Rezeug.

CHAPTER XVII

Undoing of Aiguillettes
(Impotence for a Time)

K NOW, O VIZIR (God be good to you!), that impotence
arises from three causes:
Firstly, from the tying of aiguillettes.[217]
Secondly, from a feeble and relaxed constitution.
And thirdly, from too premature ejaculation.

To cure the tying of aiguillettes you must take *galanga*,[218] cinnamon from Mecca, cloves, Indian cachou,[219] nutmeg, Indian
cubebs, sparrow-wort,[220] cinnamon, Persian pepper, Indian
thistle,[221] cardamoms,[222] pyrether, laurel-seed, and gilly-flowers.

---

[217] It happens sometimes at the encounter of man and woman that the
former, though burning with desire, cannot accomplish the act of coition,
owing to the state of inertia resisting all incitement to which his member
is reduced. It is then said of him that his *aiguillette* (needle) is tied.

[218] The *galanga* is an Indian root. There are two kinds: the *galanga
major* and the *galanga minor*.

[219] The *cachou*, from the Indian *catché*, or the Brazilian *cajou*, is a
vegetable substance which comes to us from India all ready.
Observation in the autograph edition: Certain texts have it, *Indian
tartar* or *Indian harehar*. It cannot be exactly determined to what substances these two names belong.

[220] See Note 215, page 238.

[221] This is the thistle which grows in the West Indies. Taken as a
decoction, this plant acts as a pectoral and an aperient.
Observation in the autograph edition: The texts which have been
consulted give as the name of the plant, the use of which is recommended,
chelass el heundi, a name for which an English equivalent could not be
found.

[222] See note 216, page 238.

All these ingredients must be pounded together carefully, and one drinks of it as much as one can, morning and night, in broth, particularly in pigeon broth; fowl broth may, however, be substituted just as well. Water is to be drunk before and after taking it. The compound may likewise be taken with honey, which is the best method, and gives the best results.

The man whose ejaculation is too precipitate must take nutmeg and incense (*oliban*)[223] mixed together with honey.

If the impotence arises from weakness, the following ingredients are to be taken in honey: viz., pyrether, nettle-seed,[224] a little spurge (or cevadille), ginger, cinnamon of Mecca, and cardamom. This preparation will cause the weakness to disappear and effect the cure, with the permission of God the Highest!

I can warrant the efficacy of all these preparations, the virtue of which has been tested.

The impossibility of performing the coitus, owing to the absence of stiffness in the member, is also due to other causes. It will happen, for instance, that a man with his verge in erection will find it getting flaccid just when he is on the point of introducing it between the thighs of the woman. He thinks this is impotence, while it is simply the result, may be, of an exaggerated respect for the woman, may be of a misplaced bashfulness, may be because one has observed something disagreeable, or on account of an unpleasant odour; finally, owing to a feeling of jealousy, inspired by the reflection that the woman is no longer a virgin, and has served the pleasures of other men.

[223] *Oliban* is mentioned in the *Journal Asiatique*, in connection with the Greek fire and gunpowder, by Messrs. Reynaud and Favet.
[224] Nettle-seed is considered by the Arabs as a remedy against the inflammation of the urethral canal.

CHAPTER XVIII

Prescriptions for Increasing the Dimensions of Small members and for making them Splendid

K NOW, O VIZIR (God be good to you!), that this chapter, which treats of the size of the virile member, is of the first importance both for men and women. For the men, because from a good-sized and vigorous member there springs the affection and love of women; for the women, because it is by such members that their amorous passions are appeased, and the greatest pleasure is procured for them. This is evident from the fact that many men, solely by reason of their insignificant members, are, as far as coition is concerned, objects of aversion to women, who likewise entertain the same sentiment with regard to those whose members are soft, nerveless, and relaxed. Their whole happiness consists in the use of robust and strong members.

A man, therefore, with a small member, who wants to make it grand or fortify it for the coitus, must rub it before copulation with tepid water, until it gets red and extended by the blood flowing into it, in consequence of the heat; he must then anoint it with a mixture of honey and ginger, rubbing it in sedulously. Then let him join the woman; he will procure for her such pleasure that she objects to him getting off her again.

Another remedy consists in a compound made of a moderate quantity of pepper, lavender, galanga, and musk, reduced to powder, sifted, and mixed up with honey and preserved ginger. The member, after having been first washed in warm water, is then vigorously rubbed with the mixture; it will then grow large and brawny, and afford to the woman a marvellous feeling of voluptuousness.

A third remedy is the following: wash the member in warm water until it becomes red, and enters into erection. Then take a piece of soft leather, upon which spread hot pitch, and envelope the member with it. It will not be long before the member raises its head, trembling with passion. The leather is to be left on until the pitch grows cold, and the member is again in a state of repose. This operation, several times repeated, will have the effect of making the member strong and thick.[225]

A fourth remedy is based upon the use made of leeches, but only of such as live in water (*sic*). You put as many of them into a bottle as can be got in, and fill it up with oil. Then expose the bottle to the sun, until the heat of the same has effected a complete mixture. With the fluid thus obtained the member is to be rubbed several consecutive days, and it will, by being thus treated, become of a good size and of full dimensions.

For another procedure I will here note the use of an ass's member. Procure one and boil it, together with onions and a large quantity of corn. With this dish feed fowls, which you eat afterwards. One can also macerate the ass's verge with oil, and use the fluid thus obtained for anointing one's member, and drinking of it.

Another way is to bruise leeches with oil, and rub the verge with this ointment; or, if it is preferred, the leeches may be put into a bottle, and, thus enclosed, buried in a warm dunghill until they are dissolved into a coherent mass and form a sort of liniment, which is used for repeatedly anointing the member. The member is certain to greatly benefit by this.

[225] A very dangerous operation, and undoubtedly completely inefficacious. Throughout the East, however, one reads of similar methods, some of which are even more dangerous, and which must, in practice, have led to some dire and tragic results. (A.H.W.)

One may likewise take rosin and wax, mixed with tubipore,[226] asphodel,[227] and cobbler's glue,[228] with which mixture rub the member, and the result will be that its dimensions will be enlarged.

The efficacy of all these remedies is well known, and I have tested them.

[226] The tubipore is a *calcareous polypus* composed of cylindrical tubes, and forming round masses, often of great size, in the sea. Its medical properties are much doubted.

Observation in the autograph edition: This substance is called in certain texts *deum el akhouine*, and is, according to the book of the physician Abd er Rezeug, the juice of a plant called *chiane*, alias *heï el âleum*; the juice goes also by the name *deum el tsâbane*. We have ascertained that *heï el âleum* signifies also the *sempervivum* (a name given to a kind of house-leek), and the literal translation of *deum el tsâbane* is 'dragon's blood.' This is all the information we could get on the subject.

[227] The asphodel (daffodil) is a plant with lilaceous flowers, coming from Italy. There is a yellow and a white kind.

Observation in the autograph edition: *Boureouk* signifies also borax and nitre.

[228] The glue used by the Mussulman cobblers to glue their leather is made of a single substance, the spleen of cattle or sheep, which they call *tihal*.

Note in the autograph edition: The only text which gives this passage calls this substance *annzeronte* or *ânnezeronte*, the rosin of the sarcocollus, which was credited with the property of making the flesh firm and healing wounds.

CHAPTER XIX

Of things that take away the Bad Smell from the Armpits and Sexual Parts of Women and Contract the Latter

K NOW, O VIZIR (God be good to you!), that bad exhalations from the vulva and of the armpits are, as also a wide
vagina, the greatest of evils.

If a woman wants this bad odour to disappear she must pound
red myrrh, then sift it, and knead this powder with myrtle-
water,[229] and rub her sexual parts with this wash. All disagreeable
emanation will disappear from her vulva.

Another remedy is obtained by pounding lavender, and knead-
ing it afterwards with musk-rose-water. Saturate a piece of
woollen-stuff with it, and rub the vulva with the same until it is
hot. The bad smell will be removed by this.

If a woman intends to contract her vagina, she has only to
dissolve alum in water, and wash her sexual parts with the
solution, which may be made still more efficacious by the addition of a little bark of the walnut-tree, the latter substance being
very astringent.

Another remedy to be mentioned is the following, which is
well known for its efficacy: Boil well in water carobs (locusts),[230]

---

[229] The author designates here, under the name of *ass*, the *myrtus com-
munis* of Linnaeus; the more usual name is *reund*, which serves also to
designate the laurel tree.
[230] The carob is the fruit of the locust-tree, a well known tree, the flowers
of which emit a penetrating odour like that of the virile sperm. The
fruit is considered to have aperient and pectoral properties, and the leaves
are astringent.

freed from their kernels, and bark of the pomegranate tree. The woman takes a sitz bath in the decoction thus obtained, and which must be as hot as she can bear it; when the bath gets cold, it must be warmed and used again, and this immersion is to be repeated several times. The same result may be obtained by fumigating the vulva with cow-dung.

To do away with the bad smell of the armpits, one takes antimony[231] and mastic, which are to be pounded together, and put with water into an earthen vase. The mixture is then rubbed against the sides of the vase until it turns red; when it is ready for use, rub it into the armpits, and the bad smell will be removed. It must be used repeatedly, until a radical cure is effected.

The same result may be arrived at by pounding together antimony (*hadida*) and mastic, setting the mixture afterwards onto a stove over a low fire, until it is of the consistency of bread, and rubbing the residue with a stone until the pellicle, which will have formed, is removed. Then rub it into the armpits, and you may be sure that the bad smell will soon be gone.

[231] Note in the autograph edition : The texts, which were consulted, name the substance in question *hadida*, by which name goes the oxide of copper of commeric, which, exposed to the action of fire, pulverised, and mixed with gall-nut, is used for dying the hair black.

CHAPTER XX

Instructions with regard to Pregnancy and how the Gender of the Child that is to be Born may be known - that is to say, Knowledge of the Sex of the Foetus

KNOW, O VIZIR (God be good to you!), that the certain indications of pregnancy are the following: the dryness of the vulva immediately after coitus, the inclination to stretch herself, accesses of somnolency, heavy and profound sleep, the frequent contraction of the opening of the vulva to such an extent that not even a *meroud* could penetrate, the nipples of the breast become darker, and lastly, the most certain of all marks is the cessation of menstruation.

If the woman remains always in good health from the time that her pregnancy is certain, if she preserves the good looks of her face and a clear complexion, if she does not become freckled, then it may be taken as a sign that the child will be a boy.

The red colour of the nipples also points to a child of the male sex. The strong development of the breasts, and bleeding from the nose, if it comes from the right nostril,[232] are signs of the same purport.

The signs pointing to the conception of a child of the female sex are numerous. I will name them here: frequent indisposition

---

[232] The right side is considered by Mussulmans as the side of good augury. See the Koran, chap. lvi, verse 26.

during pregnancy, pale complexion, spots and freckles, pains in the matrix, frequent nightmares, blackness of the nipples, a heavy feeling on the left side, nasal hemorrhage on the same side.

If there is any doubt about the pregnancy, let the woman drink, on going to bed, honey-water, and if then she has a feeling of heaviness in the abdomen, it is a proof that she is with child. If the right side feels heavier than the left one, it will be a boy. If the breasts are swelling with milk, this is similarly a sign that the child she is bearing will be of the male sex.

I have received this information from savants, and all the indications are positive and tested.

CHAPTER XXI

*Forming the Conclusion of this Work, and
Treating of the Good Effects of the Deglutition
of Eggs as Favourable to the Coitus*

KNOW, O VIZIR (God be good to you!), that this chapter
contains the most useful instructions – how to increase the
intensity of the coitus – and that the latter part is profitable
to read for an old man as well as for the man in his best years
and for the young man.

The *Cheikh*, who gives good advice to the creatures of God the
Great! he the sage, the savant, the first of the men of his time,
speaks as follows on this subject; listen then to his words:

He who makes it a practice to eat every day fasting the yolks
of eggs, without the white part, will find in this aliment an
energetic stimulant towards coitus. The same is the case with the
man who during three days eats of the same mixed with onions.

He who boils asparagus,[233] and then fries them in fat, and then
pours upon them the yolks of eggs with pounded condiments,
and eats every day of this dish, will grow very strong for the
coitus, and find in it a stimulant for his amorous desires.

He who peels onions, puts them into a saucepan, with condi-

---

[233] Note in the autograph edition: The Arab text has *heïloun*. The medical dictionary of Abd er Rezeug says about *helioun*: 'Helioun, and in
placing the *ia* (in) more forward, making it *heïloun*, is in the medical, but
not in the general sense, asparagus.' So we have adopted this meaning, in
preference to boiled meal as translated, and which meaning we could not
find, although we searched carefully for it in the Arab books.

ments and aromatic substances, and fries the mixture with oil and yolks of eggs, will acquire a surpassing and invaluable vigour for the coitus, if he will partake of this dish for several days.

Camel's-milk mixed with honey and taken regularly develops a vigour for copulation which is unaccountable and causes the virile member to be on the alert night and day.

He who for several days makes his meals upon eggs boiled with myrrh, coarse cinnamon, and pepper, will find his vigour with respect to coition and erections greatly increased. He will have a feeling as though his member would never return to a state of repose.

A man who wishes to copulate during a whole night, and whose desire, having come on suddenly, will not allow him to prepare himself and follow the regimen just mentioned, may have recourse to the following recipe. He must get a great number of eggs, so that he may eat to surfeit, and fry them with fresh fat and butter; when done he immerses them in honey, working the whole mass well together. He must then eat of them as much as possible with a little bread, and he may be certain that for the whole night his member will not give him any rest.

On this subject the following verses have been composed:

> The member of Abou el Heïloukh has remained erect
> For thirty days without a break, because he did eat onions.
> Abou el Heïdja has deflowered[234] in one night
> Once eighty virgins, and he did not eat or drink between,
> Because he'd surfeited himself first with chick-peas,
> And had drunk camel's milk with honey mixed.
> Mimoun, the negro, never ceased to spend his sperm, while he
> For fifty days without a truce the game was working.
> How proud he was to finish such a task!
> For ten days more he worked it,[235] not was he yet surfeited,
> But all this time he ate but yolk of eggs and bread.[236]

[234] The text says, Abou el Heïdja deflowered eighty virgins straight, that is to say, from the front in the natural way.

Observation in the autograph edition: The texts, which we have consulted, say 'entirely.'

[235] 'Depuys luy Aristoteles,' etc. (*Rabelais*, book iii, chap. 27).

[236] Note in the autograph edition: It is to be observed that in these verses, as similarly in all the other verses which appear in the work, the

The deeds of Abou el Heïloukh, Abou el Heïdja and Mimoun, just cited, have been justly praised, and their history is truly marvellous. So I will make you acquainted with it, please God, and thus complete the signal services which this work is designed to render to humanity.

The History of Zohra

The *Cheikh*, the protector of religion (God, the Highest, be good to him!) records, that there lived once in remote antiquity an illustrious King, who had numerous armies and immense riches.

This King had seven daughters remarkable for their beauty and perfections. These seven had been borne one after another, without any male infant between them.

The Kings of the time wanted them in marriage, but they refused to be married. They wore men's clothing, rode on magnificent horses covered with gold-embroidered trappings, knew how to handle the sword and the spear, and bore men down in single combat. Each of them possessed a splendid palace with the servants and slaves necessary for such service, for the preparation of meat and drink, and other necessities of that kind.

Whenever a marriage-offer for one of them was presented to the King, he never failed to consult with her about it; but they always answered, 'That shall never be.'

Different conclusions were drawn from these refusals; some in a good sense, some in a bad one.

For a long time no positive information could be gathered of the reasons for this conduct, and the daughters persevered in acting in the same manner until the death of their father. Then the oldest of them was called upon to succeed him, and received the oath of fidelity from all his subjects. This accession to the throne resounded through all the countries.

The name of the eldest sister was Fouzel Djemal (the flower

line is always broken at the hemistich, and not at the verse, as the Arab language admits in the verse two quite distinct parts, which are, at least in theory, equal in rhythm.

of beauty); the second was called Soltana el Agmar (the queen of moons); the third, Bediâat el Djemal (the incomparable in beauty); the fourth, Ouarda (the rose); the fifth, Mahmouda (the praiseworthy); the sixth, Kamela (the perfect); and, finally, the seventh, Zohra (the beauty).

Zohra, the youngest, was at the same time the most intelligent and judicious.

She was passionately fond of the chase, and one day as she was riding through the fields she met on her way a cavalier, who saluted her, and she returned his salute; she had some twenty men in her service with her. The cavalier thought it was the voice of a woman he had heard, but as Zohra's face was covered by a flap of her *haïk*,[237] he was not certain, and said to himself, 'I would like to know whether this is a woman or a man.' He asked one of the princess's servants, who dissipated his doubts. Approaching Zohra, he then conversed pleasantly with her till they made a halt for breakfast. He sat down near her to partake of the repast.

Disappointing the hopes of the cavalier, the princess did not uncover her face, and, pleading that she was fasting, ate nothing. He could not help admiring secretly her hand, the gracefulness of her waist, and the amorous expression of her eyes. His heart was seized with a violent love.

The following conversation took place between them:

The Cavalier: 'Is your heart insensible for friendship?'

Zohra: 'It is not proper for a man to feel friendship for a woman; for if their hearts once incline towards each other, libidinous desires will soon invade them, and with Satan enticing them to do wrong, their fall is soon known by everyone.'

The Cavalier: 'It is not so, when the affection is true and their intercourse pure without infidelity or treachery.'

Zohra: 'If a woman gives way to the affection she feels for

---

[237] The *haïk* is a long piece of a light and white material, generally of wool or silk, with which the Arabs envelop body and head, and over which they wear the *burnous*.

a man, she becomes an object of slander for the whole world, and of general contempt, whence nothing arises but trouble and regrets.'

The Cavalier: 'But our love will remain secret, and in this retired spot, which may serve us as our place of meeting, we shall have intercourse together unknown to all.'

Zohra: 'That may not be. Besides, it could not so easily be done, we should soon be suspected, and the eyes of the whole world would be turned upon us.'

The Cavalier: 'But love, love is the source of life. The happiness, that is, the meeting, the embraces, the caresses of lovers. The sacrifice of the fortune, and even of the life for your love.'

Zohra: 'These words are impregnated with love, and your smile is seductive; but you would do better to refrain from similar conversation.'

The Cavalier: 'Your word is emerald and your counsels are sincere. But love has now taken root in my heart, and no one is able to tear it out. If you drive me from you I shall assuredly die.'

Zohra: 'For all that you must return to your place and I to mine. If it pleases God we shall meet again.'[238]

They then separated, bidding each other adieu, and returned each of them to their dwelling.

The cavalier's name was Abou el Heïdja. His father, Kheiroun, was a great merchant and immensely rich, whose habitation stood isolated beyond the estate of the princess, a day's journey distant from her castle. Abou el Heïdja returned home, could not rest, and put on again his *temeur*[239] when the night fell, took a black turban, and buckled his sword on under his *temeur*. Then he mounted his horse, and, accompanied by his favourite negro, Mimoun, he rode away secretly under the cover of night.

[238] Note in the autograph edition: The greater part of this dialogue is written in rhymed prose.

[239] The *temeur* is a woollen vestment used by Orientals to keep off the cold on their journeys.

Observation in the autograph edition: They are generally old vestments which are used on such occasions, and are thus called.

They travelled all night without stopping until, on the approach of daylight, the dawn came upon them in sight of Zohra's castle. They then made a halt among the hills, and entered with their horses into a cavern which they found there.

Abou el Heïdja left the negro in charge of the horses, and went in the direction of the castle, in order to examine its approaches; he found it surrounded by a very high wall. Not being able to get into it, he retired to some distance to watch those who came out. But the whole day passed away and he saw no one come out.

After sunset he sat himself down at the entrance of the cavern and kept on the watch until midnight; then sleep overcame him.

He was lying asleep with his head on Mimoun's knee, when the latter suddenly awakened him. 'What is it?' he asked. 'O my master,' said Mimoun, 'I have heard some noise in the cavern, and I saw the glimmer of a light.' He rose at once, and looking attentively, he perceived indeed a light, towards which he went, and which guided him to a recess in the cavern. Having ordered the negro to wait for him while he was going to find out where it proceeded from, he took his sabre and penetrated deeper into the cavern. He discovered a subterranean vault, into which he descended.

The road to it was nearly impracticable, on account of the stones which encumbered it. He contrived, however, after much trouble to reach a kind of crevice, through which the light shone which he had perceived. Looking through it, he saw the princess Zohra, surrounded by about a hundred virgins. They were in a magnificent palace dug out in the heart of the mountain, splendidly furnished and resplendent with gold everywhere. The maidens were eating and drinking and enjoying the pleasures of the table.

Abou el Heïdja said to himself, 'Alas! I have no companion to assist me at this difficult moment.' Under the influence of this reflection, he returned to his servant, Mimoun, and said to him,

'Go to my brother before God,[240] Abou el Heïloukh, and tell him to come here to me as quickly as he can.' The servant forthwith mounted upon his horse, and rode through the remainder of the night.

Of all his friends, Abou el Heïloukh was the one whom Abou el Heïdja liked best; he was the son of the Vizir. This young man and Abou el Heïdja and the negro, Mimoun, passed as the three strongest and most fearless men of their time, and no one ever succeeded in overcoming them in combat.

When the negro Mimoun came to his master's friend, and had told him what had happened, the latter said, 'Certainly, we belong to God and shall return to him.' Then he took his sabre, mounted his horse, and taking his favourite negro with him, he made his way, with Mimoun, to the cavern.

Aboul el Heïdja came out to meet him and bid him welcome, and having informed him of the love he bore to Zohra, he told him of his resolution to penetrate forcibly into the palace, of the circumstances under which he had taken refuge in the cavern, and the marvellous scene he had witnessed while there. Abou el Heïloukh was dumb with surprise.

At nightfall they heard singing, boisterous laughter, and animated talking. Abou el Heïdja said to his friend, 'Go to the end of the subterranean passage and look. You will then make excuse for the love of your brother.' Abou el Heïloukh stealing softly down to the lower end of the grotto, looked into the interior of the palace, and was enchanted with the sight of these virgins and their charms. 'O brother,' he asked, 'which among these women is Zohra?'

Abou el Heïdja answered, 'The one with the irreproachable shape, whose smile is irresistible, whose cheeks are roses, and whose forehead is resplendently white, whose head is encircled by a crown of pearls, and whose garments sparkle with gold. She is seated on a throne incrusted with rare stones and nails of silver, and she is leaning her head upon her hand.'

[240] Among the Arabs the name of 'brother' is very usual between friends.

'I have observed her of all the others,' said Abou el Heïloukh, 'as though she were a standard or a blazing torch. But, O my brother, let me draw your attention to a matter which appears not to have struck you.' 'What is it?' asked Abou el Heïdja. His friend replied, 'It is very certain, O my brother, that licentiousness reigns in this palace. Observe that these people come here only at night time, and that this is a retired place. There is every reason to believe that it is exclusively consecrated to feasting, drinking, and debauchery, and if it was your idea that you could have come to her you love by any other way than the one on which we are now, you would have found that you had deceived yourself, even if you had found means to communicate with her by the help of other people.' 'And why so?' asked Abou el Heïdja. 'Because,' said his friend, 'as far as I can see, Zohra solicits the affection of young girls, which is a proof that she can have no inclination for men, nor be responsive to their love.'

'O Abou el Heïloukh,' said Abou el Heïdja, 'I know the value of your judgment, and it is for that I have sent for you. You know that I have never hesitated to follow your advice and counsel!' 'O my brother,' said the son of the Vizir, 'if God had not guided you to this entrance of the palace, you would never have been able to approach Zohra. But from here, please God! we can find our way.'

Next morning, at sunrise, they ordered their servants to make a breach in that place, and managed to get everything out of the way that could obstruct the passage. This done they hid their horses in another cavern, safe from wild beasts and thieves; then all the four, the two masters and the two servants, entered the cavern and penetrated into the palace, each of them armed with sabre and buckler. They then closed up again the breach, and restored its former appearance.

Now they found themselves in darkness, but Abou el Heïloukh, having struck a match, lighted one of the candles, and they began to explore the palace in every sense. It seemed to them the marvel of marvels. The furniture was magnificent. Everywhere there were beds and couches of all kinds, rich candelabras, splendid lustres, sumptuous carpets, and tables covered with dishes, fruits and beverages.

When they had admired all these treasures, they went on examining the chambers, counting them. There was a great number of them, and in the last one they found a secret door, very small, and of appearance which attracted their attention. Abou el Heïloukh said, 'This is very probably the door which communicates with the palace. Come, O my brother, we will await the things that are to come in one of these chambers.' They took their position in a cabinet difficult of access, high up, and from which one could see without being seen.

So they waited till night came on. At that moment the secret door opened, giving admission to a negress carrying a torch, who set alight all the lustres and candelabra, arranged the beds, set the plates, placed all sorts of meats upon the tables, with cups and bottles, and perfumed the air with the sweetest scents.

Soon afterwards the maidens made their appearance. Their gait denoted at the same time indifference and languor. They seated themselves upon the divans, and the negress offered them meat and drink. They ate, drank, and sang melodiously.

Then the four men, seeing them giddy with wine, came down from their hiding place with their sabres in their hands, brandishing them over the heads of the maidens. They had first taken care to veil their faces with the upper part of their *haïk*.

'Who are these men,' cried Zohra, 'who are invading our dwelling under cover of the shades of the night? Have you risen out of the ground, or did you descend from the sky? What do you want?'

'Coition!' they answered.

'With whom?' asked Zohra.

'With you, O apple of my eye!' said Abou el Heïdja, advancing.

Zohra: 'Who are you?'

The princess, turning then to the negro Mimoun, asked, 'And this one, what is his name?' They said, 'Mimoun.' 'Your task shall be,' said the princess, pointing to Mouna, 'to do this woman's business without resting for fifty consecutive days; you need not ejaculate unless you like; but if the excess of fatigue forces you to stop, you will not have fulfilled your obligations.' They all cried out at the hardness of such a task; but Mimoun protested, and said, 'I accept the condition, and shall come out of it with honour!' The fact was that this negro had an insatiable appetite for the coitus. Zohra told him to go with Mouna to her chamber, impressing upon the latter to let her know if the negro should exhibit the slightest trace of fatigue.

'And you, what is your name?' she asked the friend of Abou el Heïdja. 'Abou el Heïloukh,' he replied. 'Well, then, Abou el Heïloukh, what I require of you is to remain here, in the presence of these women and virgins, for thirty consecutive days, with your member during this period always in erection during day and night.'

Then she said to the fourth, 'What is your name?'

'Felah (good fortune),' was his answer. 'Very well, Felah,' she said, 'you will remain at our disposition for any services which we may have to demand of you.'

However, Zohra, in order to leave no motive for any excuse, and so that she might not be accused of bad faith, had asked them, first of all, what regimen they wished to follow during the period of their trial. Abou el Heïdja had asked for the only drink – excepting water – camel's milk with honey, and, for nourishment, chick-peas cooked with meat and abundance of onions; and, by means of these aliments he did, by the permission of God, accomplish his remarkable exploit. Abou el Heïloukh demanded, for his nourishment, onions cooked with meat, and, for drink, the juice pressed out of pounded onions mixed with honey. Mimoun, on his part, asked for yolks of eggs and bread.

However, Abou el Heïdja claimed of Zohra the favour of

'I am Abou el Heïdja.'

Zohra: 'But how is it you know me?'

'It is I who met you while out hunting at such and suc
place.'

Zohra: 'But what brought you hither?'

'The will of God the Highest!'

At this answer Zohra was silent, and set herself to think
means by which she could rid herself of these intruders.

Now among the virgins that were present there were sev
whose vulvas were like iron barred,[241] and whom no one had l
able to deflower; there was also present a woman called Mc
(she who appeases the passion), who was insatiable as reg
coition. Zohra thought to herself, 'It is only by a stratage
can get rid of these men. By means of these women I wil
them tasks which they will be unable to accomplish as cc
tions for my consent.' Then turning to Abou el Heïdja, she
to him, 'You will not get possession of me unless you fulfil
conditions which I shall impose upon you.' The four cava
at once consented to this without knowing them, and she
tinued, 'But, if you do not fulfil them, will you pledge your v
that you will be my prisoners, and place yourselves entirel
my disposition?' 'We pledge our words!' they answered.

She made them take their oath that they would be faithf
their word, and then, placing her hand in that of Abou el He
she said to him, 'As regards you, I impose upon you the tas
deflowering eighty virgins without ejaculating. Such is my w
He answered, 'I accept.'

She let him then enter a chamber where there were se
kinds of beds, and sent to him the eighty virgins in success
Abou el Heïdja deflowered them all, and so ravished in a si
night the maidenhood of eighty young girls without ejacula
the smallest drop of sperm. This extraordinary vigour f
Zohra with astonishment, and likewise all those who
present.

[241] Note in the autograph edition: Literally, 'ironbound,' *mouseaha*

R

copulating with her on the strength of the fact that he had fulfilled his engagement. She answered him, 'Oh, impossible! the condition which you have fulfilled is inseparable from those which your companions have to comply with. The agreement must be carried out in its entirety, and you will find me true to my promise. But if one amongst you should fail in his task, you will all be my prisoners by the will of God!'

Abou el Heïdja gave way in the face of this firm resolve, and sat down amongst the girls and women, and ate and drank with them, whilst waiting for the conclusion of the tasks of his companions.

At first Zohra, feeling convinced that they would soon all be at her mercy, was all amiability and smiles. But when the twentieth day had come she began to show signs of distress; and on the thirtieth she could no longer restrain her tears. For on that day Abou el Heïloukh had finished his task, and, having come out of it honourably, he took his seat by the side of his friend amongst the company, who continued to eat tranquilly and to drink abundantly.

From that time the princess, who had now no other hope than in the failure of the negro Mimoun, relied upon his becoming fatigued before he finished his work. She sent every day to Mouna for information, who sent word that the negro's vigour was constantly increasing, and she began to despair, seeing already Abou el Heïdja and Abou el Heïloukh coming off as victors in their enterprises. One day she said to the two friends, 'I have made inquiries about the negro, and Mouna has let me know that he was exhausted with fatigue.' At these words Abou el Heïdja cried, 'In the name of God! if he does not carry out his task, aye, and if he does not go beyond it for ten days longer, he shall die the vilest of deaths!'

But his zealous servant never during the period of fifty days took any rest in his work of copulation, and kept going on, besides, for ten days longer, as ordered by his master. Mouna, on her part, had the greatest satisfaction, as this feat had at last appeased her ardour for coition.[242] Mimoun, having remained victor, could then take his seat with his companions.

Then said Abou el Heïdja to Zohra. 'See, we have fulfilled all the conditions you have imposed upon us. It is now for you to accord me the favours which, according to our agreement, was to be the price if we succeeded.' 'It is but too true!' answered the princess, and she gave herself up to him, and he found her excelling the most excellent.[243]

As to the negro, Mimoun, he married Mouna. Abou el Heïloukh chose, amongst all the virgins, the one whom he had found most attractive.

They all remained in the palace, giving themselves up to good cheer and all possible pleasures, until death put an end to their happy existence and dissolved their union. God be merciful to them[244] as well as to all Mussulmans! Amen!

It is to this story that the verses cited previously make allusion.[245] I have given it here, because it testifies to the efficacy of the dishes and remedies, the use of which I have recommended, for giving vigour for coition, and all learned men agree in acknowledging their salutary effects.

There are still other beverages of excellent virtue. I will des-

[242] Note in the autograph edition: In certain texts the following version is found: 'Mouna, at the end of the fifty days, was glad to have come to the end of the trial, for she had become sick of coitus; but as Mimoun kept going on, she sent to Zohra the message, "O my mistress, the time has elapsed, and he will not part with me! I conjure you, by God the Magnificent, withdraw me from this grievous situation. My thighs are like broken, and it becomes impossible for me to keep lying down." But Mimoun swore that he would not retire until the ten days ordered by his master were gone, and he kept his word.'

[243] Note in the autograph edition: Another version says here: 'The performance of Mimoun filled all the world with admiration. They then took possession of everything contained in the castle; treasures, women, servants, the girls and all. They divided the whole into equal parts, of which each took his share; then Abou el Heïdja had his pleasure with Zohra, and he found her, etc.'

[244] When pronouncing the name of a dead co-religionist, the Mussulmans never fail to add, 'God be merciful to him!' (*Allah irahmou!*)

[245] Note in the autograph edition: It must be observed that certain particulars as given in the verses are not in perfect accordance with the corresponding parts in the story.

cribe the following: Take one part of the juice pressed out of pounded onions, and mix it with two parts of purified honey. Heat the mixture over a fire until the onion-juice has disappeared and the honey only remains. Then take the residue from the fire, let it get cool, and preserve it for use when wanted. Then mix of the same one *aoukia*[246] with three *aouak* of water, and let chickpeas be macerated in this fluid for one day and one night.

This beverage is to be partaken of during winter and on going to bed. Only a small quantity is to be taken, and only for one day. The member of him who has drunk of it will not give him much rest during the night that follows. As to the man who partakes of it for several consecutive days, he will constantly have his member rigid and upright without intermission. A man with an ardent temperament ought not to make use of it, as it may give him a fever. Nor should the medicine be used three days in succession except by old or cold-tempered men. And lastly, it should not be resorted to in summer.

> I certainly did wrong to put this book together;
> But you will pardon me, nor let me pray in vain,
> O God ! award no punishment for this on judgment day !
> And thou, oh reader, hear me conjure thee to say : So be it ![247]

[246] Note in the autograph edition: *Aoukia*, derived from the Greek.
[247] *Id*. These verses form the end of the most complete manuscript which we had in our hands.

APPENDIX TO THE AUTOGRAPH EDITION

To the Reader

IN THE YEAR of grace 1876 some amateurs who were passionately fond of Arabian literature combined for the purpose of reproducing, by autographic process, a number of copies of a French translation of a work written by the Cheikh Nefzaoui, which book had, by a lucky chance, fallen into their hands. Each brought to the undertaking such assistance as his special knowledge allowed, and it was thus that a tedious work was achieved by amateurs, amidst obstacles which were calculated to abate the ardour of their enthusiasm.

Thus, as the reader has doubtless already divined, it was not an individual, but a concourse of individuals, who, taking advantage of a union of favourable circumstances and facilities, not of common occurrence, offered to their friends the first fruit of a work, interesting, and of such rarity that to the present time very few have had the opportunity of reading it, while they could only gather their knowledge from incorrect manuscripts, sophisticated copies, and incomplete translations! It is to this association of efforts, guided by the principle of the division of labour for the carrying out of a great undertaking, that the appearance of this book is due.

The Editor (it is under this name that the Society J.M.P.Q.[248]

[248] It has been said that the initial 'M' in the initials of the above Society indicates the word '*Maréchal*' – i.e. the Commandant Maréchal of Guy de Maupassant's letter. The copy which Maupassant saw was magnificently bound, and bore on its cover a monogram containing the four initials

has been, is, and will be designated) is assured beforehand, notwithstanding the imperfection of his production, of the sympathies of his readers, who are all friends of his, or friends of his friends, and for whose benefit he has worked. For this reason he is not going to claim an indulgence which has been already extended to him; his wish is only to make clear to everybody the exact value and nature of the book which he is offering, and to make known on what foundations the work has been done, in how far the remarkable translation of M—— has been respected, and, in short, what reliance may be placed in the title, 'Translated from the Arabic by M——, Staff Officer.'

It is, in fact, important that there should be no misunderstanding on this point, and that the reader should not imagine that he holds an exact copy of that translation in his hands; for we confess that we have modified it, and we give these explanations in order to justify the alterations which were imposed by the attending circumstances.

As far as we are aware, there have been made until now only two proper translations of the work of the Cheikh Nefzaoui. One, of which we have availed ourselves, is due, as is well known, to M——, a fanatical and distinguished Arabophile; the other is the work of Doctor L——; the latter we have never seen.

A learned expounder commenced a translation which promised to leave the others far behind. Unfortunately, death interrupted the accomplishment of this work, and there was no one to continue it.

Our intention, at the outset, was to reproduce simply the first of the aforenamed translations, making, however, such rectifications as were necessitated by gross mistakes in the orthography, and in the French idiom, by which the manuscript in our possession was disfigured. Our views did not go beyond that; but

indicated, each of which probably signified one of the four gentlemen who collaborated in the production of the autograph edition. It has also been said that the 'M' may indicate the name of a 'Commandant Marécla – Commandant Supérieur du Cercle Militaire de Bou-Saâda'. (A.H.W.)

we had scarcely made any progress with the book when we found that it was impossible to keep to the translation as it stood. Obvious omissions, mistaken renderings of the sense, originating, no doubt, with the faulty Arab text which the translator had at his disposal, and which were patent at first sight, imposed upon us the necessity of consulting other resources. We were thus induced to examine all the Arab manuscripts of the work which we could by any possibility obtain.

Three texts were to this end put under contribution. These treated of the same subjects in the same order, and presented the same succession of chapters, corresponding, however, in this respect, point by point, with the manuscript upon which our translator had to work; but while two of them gave a kind of abstract of the questions treated, the third, on the contrary, seemed to enlarge at pleasure upon every subject.

We shall expatiate to some slight extent upon this last named text, since the study of it has enabled us to clear up a certain number of points upon which M——, not withstanding his conscientious researches, has been unable to throw sufficient light.

The principal characteristic of this text, which is not exempt from gross mistakes, is the affectation of more care as to style and choice of expressions; it enters more into fastidious, and frequently technical particulars, contains more quotations of verses – often, be it remarked, inapplicable ones – and uses, in certain circumstances, filthy images, which seem to have had a particular attraction for the author; but as a compensation for these faults, it gives, instead of cold, dry explications, pictures which are often charming, wanting neither in poetry nor originality, nor in descriptive talent, nor even in a certain elevation of thought, and bearing an undeniable stamp of originality. We may cite as an example the 'Chapter on Kisses,' which is found neither in our translation nor in the other two texts which we have examined, and which we have borrowed.

In our character as Gauls, we must not complain about the obscenities which are scattered about, as if on purpose to excite

the grosser passions; but what we must deprecate are the tedious
expansions, whole pages full of verbiage, which disfigure the
work, and are like the reverse of the medal. The author has felt
this himself, as at the conclusion of his work he requests the
reader to pardon him in consideration of the good intention
which has guided his pen. In presence of the qualities of first
rank which must be acknowledged to exist in the book, we
should have preferred that it had not contained these defects;
we should have liked, in one word, to see it more homogeneous
and more earnest; and more particularly so if one considers that
the circumstance which we are pointing out raises doubts as to
the veritable origin of the new matters which have been discovered, and which might easily be taken for interpolations due
to the fancy of one or more of the copyists through whose hands
the work passed before we received it.

Everyone knows, in fact, the grave inconveniences attaching
to manuscripts, and the services rendered by the art of printing
to science and literature by disposing of them. No copy leaves
the hands of the copyist complete and perfect, particularly if
the writer is an Arab, the least scrupulous of all. The Arab
copyist not only involuntarily scatters about mistakes which are
due to his ignorance and carelessness, but will not shrink from
making corrections, modifications, and even additions, according
to his fancy. The literary reader himself, carried away by the
charm of the subject, often annotates the text in the margin,
inserts an anecdote or idea which is just current, or some puffed-
up medical recipe; and all this, to the great detriment of its
purity, finds its way into the body of the work through the
hands of the next copyist.

There can be no doubt that the work of the Cheikh Nefzaoui
has suffered in this way. Our three texts and the one upon which
the translator worked, offer striking dissimilarities, and of all
kinds; although, by the way, one of the translations seems to
approach more nearly in style to the extended text of which we
have spoken. But a question of another sort comes before us with

respect to this last, which contains more than four times as much matter as the others. Is this the entire work of the Cheikh Nefzaoui, always bearing in mind the modification to which manuscripts are exposed, and does it so stand by itself as a work for the perusal of voluptuaries, while the others are only abridged copies for the use of the vulgar, serving them as an elementary treatise? Or might it not be the product of numerous successive additions to the original work, by which, as we have already suggested, its bulk has been considerably increased.

We have no hesitation in pronouncing in favour of the first of these hypotheses. In the record which the Cheikh gives of it, he says that this is the second work of the kind which he has composed, and that it is in fact only the first one, entitled the *Torch of the Universe*, considerably increased in pursuance of the advice given him by the Vizir Mohammed ben Ouana ez Zouaoui. Might it not be possible that a third work, still more complete than the second, had been the outcome of new studies of the author? Subjects of a particular specialty have certainly been treated in the work of which we speak. In looking at the Notes which serve as a preface to this translation, we find reproaches addressed by the translator to the author, because he has merely hinted at two questions of more than ordinary interest, viz., tribady and paederasty. Well, then, the Cheikh would meet his critic triumphantly by appearing before him with the work in question, for the chapter which constitutes by itself more than half of its whole volume is the twenty-first, and bears the superscription: 'The twenty-first and last chapter of the book, treating of the utility of eggs and some other substances which favour coitus; of tribady and the woman who first conceived this description of voluptuousness; of paederasty and matters concerned with it; of procuresses and the sundry ruses by which one may get possession of a woman; of facetiae, jokes, anecdotes, and several questions concerning coitus in general.'

What would be the surprise of the translator to find a community of views and sentiments existing between himself, a representative of modern civilization, and this Arab, who lived more than three hundred years ago. He could only express his regret for having entertained so bad an opinion of his master, for having believed for one moment in an omission on his part, and for having doubted his competency to deal with the various questions spoken of.

Does not the discovery of a text so complete authorise us to admit the existence of two works, one elementary, the other learned? And might it not be by reason of a little remnant of bashfulness, that the author has reserved for the twenty-first chapter without any previous allusion, the remarkable subjects which we do not find hinted at in any other place?

To put the question in this fashion is at the same time to solve it, and to solve it in the affirmative. That interminable chapter would not be a product of interpolations. It is too long and too serious a work to admit of such a supposition. The little that we have seen of it seems to bear the stamp of a well-pronounced originality, and to be composed with too much method, not to be the work – and entirely the work – of the master.

One may be surprised that this text is so rare, but the answer is very simple. As the translator judiciously observes in his notice, the matters treated in the twenty-first chapter are of a nature to startle many people. See! an Arab, who practises in secret paederasty, affects in public rigid and austere manners, while he discusses without constraint in his conversation everything that concerns the natural coitus. Thus you will easily understand that he would not wish to be suspected of reading such a book, by which his reputation would be compromised in the eyes of his co-religionists while he would, without hesitation, exhibit a book which treated of the coitus only. Another consideration, moreover, suffices to completely explain the rarity of the work; its compass makes it very expensive, and the manuscript is not attainable by everybody on account of the high price it reaches.

However it may be as regards the origin of the text, having the three documents in our possession we have given careful revision to the translation of M——. Each doubtful point has been the object of minute research, and has been generally cleared up by one or the other. When there were several acceptable versions, we chose that which was the most fit for the context, and many mutilated passages were restored. Nor were we afraid to make additions in borrowing from the extended text what appeared to us worthy of reproduction, and for the omission of which we should have been blamed by the reader. We were careful, however, not to overload the work, and to introduce no new matter which would militate against the peculiar character of the original translation. It is partly for this last reason, and still more so because the work required for this undertaking surpassed our strength, that we could not bring to light, to our great regret, the treasures concealed in the twenty-first chapter, as well as a certain number of new tales not less acceptable than those which we have given, and with which we have enriched the text.

We must not conceal that, leaving out of sight these alterations, we have not scrupled to refine the phrases, round off the periods, correct the phraseology, and, in short, to amend even the form of the translation which, in many instances, left much to be desired. It was a matter of necessity that the perusal of the contents of the book should be made agreeable. Now, the translator, with the most praise-worthy intentions, had been too anxious to render the Arabic text, with its short jumbled sentences, as clearly as possible, and had thus made the reading painfully laborious. Looking at some passages, it may even be supposed that he had only jotted them down, particularly towards the end, and had not been able, for some reason or other, to revise them until it was too late.

The new matter introduced has compelled us to make modifications in the notes of the translator, and to add new notes for the better elucidation of the subjects which had not been treated before. We have been, with respect to these notes, as careful as we were with respect to the text, endeavouring to respect as much as possible the personal work of the translator.

Now that the reader has all the necessary information about the French edition of the Cheikh Nefzaoui's work, he will permit us to make, in conclusion, a few remarks upon the *ensemble* of the book.

There are found in it many passages which are not attractive. The extraordinary ideas displayed – for instance, those about medicines and concerning the meanings of dreams – clash too directly with modern thought not to awaken in the reader a feeling more of boredom than of pleasure.

The work is certainly encumbered with a quantity of matter which cannot but appear ridiculous in the eyes of the civilised modern reader; but we should not have been justified in weeding it out. We were bound to keep it intact as we had received it from our translator. We have held with the Italian proverb, *Traduttore, traditore*, that a work loses sufficient of its originality by being conveyed from its own tongue into another, and we hope that the plan we have adopted will meet with general approval. Those oddities are, moreover, instructive, as they make us acquainted with the manner and character of the Arab under a peculiar aspect, and not only of the Arab who was contemporary with our author, but also with the Arab of our own day. The latter is, in fact, not much more advanced than was the former. Although our contact with the race becomes closer every day in Tunis, Morocco, Egypt, and other Mussulman countries, they hold to their old medical prescriptions, have the same belief in divination, and honour the same mass of ridiculous notions, in which sorcery and amulets play a large part, and which appear to us supremely absurd. At the same time, one may observe from the very passages which we here refer to, that this people was not so averse as one might believe to witticisms, for the pun (calembour) occupies an important position in the explanations of dreams with which the author has studded the chapters on the sexual organs, apparently for no particular reason, but no doubt with the idea that no matter of interest should be absent from his work.

The reader will perhaps also find that probability is frequently sacrificed to imagination. This is a distinctive mark in Arabic literature, and our work could not otherwise but exhibit the faults inherent in the genius of this race, which revels in the love for the marvellous, and amongst whose chief literary productions are to be counted the *Thousand and one Nights*. But if these tales show such defaults very glaringly, they exhibit, on the other hand, charming qualities: simplicity, grace, delicacy; a mine of precious things which has been explored and made use of by many modern authors. We have pointed out, in some notes, the relationship which we found between these tales and those of Boccaccio and La Fontaine, but we could not draw attention to all. We had to pass over many with silence, and amongst them some of the most striking, as for instance in the case of 'The Man Expert in Stratagems Duped by his Wife,' which we find reproduced with all the perfect mastership of Balzac at the end of the *Physiologie du Mariage*.

We will not pursue this sketch any further. If instead of commencing the book with a preface we have preferred to address the reader at the end, this was done in order not to impose our views upon him and thus to stand between him and the work. Whether these additional lines will be read by him or not, we believe that we have done our duty by informing him of the direction we gave to our work. We tried, on the one hand, to prove the merits of the translator who furnished the basis for our labours, that is to say, the part which required the most science and study; while, on the other hand, we desired our readers to know in how far his translation had to be recast.

To the Arabophile who would wish to produce a better translation the way is left open; and in perfecting the work he is free to uncover the unknown beauties of the twenty-first chapter to his admiring contemporaries.